W9-CBB-375

To:____

From:____

Please accept this invitation to this very special,
very powerful book.

The Highest Calling

The HIGHEST CALLING

An inspirational novel about business and life; struggle and success.

Lawrence Janesky

TheHighestCallingBook.com

Written by Lawrence Janesky, June 17, 2009 – July 17, 2009
Layout and design by Scott Clark

First Edition

For bulk sales, group sales, or sales to schools, contact:
Relia-Serve™ Corporation, 25 Progress Ave., Seymour CT, 06483

Prologue

I was on a long flight from Alaska in early September of 2009, returning from a father and son trip. My son, Tanner, was in the window seat, I sat in the center, and a friendly woman from Tennessee sat in the aisle seat. Her name was Marilyn; a nurse recently turned manager of nurses.

We exchanged photos and stories from our Alaska adventures. Later, she took out a book. Before she started to read, she told me about it.

"I wrote a book", I said. She asked me about it, and I began telling her the story verbally. She was more than interested, and wanted me to continue. I love the story too, and I pressed on, telling her what happened next.

Then I remembered I had my Kindle™ *(digital reading device)* with my book on it. "Why don't you read the last three chapters yourself?" I pretended to leave her alone, but my eyes were off to the left, reading as she did.

When she finished, she was crying – and so was I.

This book is special. I hope it will be special to you too.

Larry Janesky

Larry Janesky
Sept 12, 2009

*To those with desire; entrepreneurs who,
while working towards their dreams in free markets,
improve the lives of everyone.*

For my mother, Leslie.

If an angel showed up to help you, *would you listen?*

Table of Contents

The HIGHEST CALLING

Chapter 1
The End

The old man lay still in the casket at the front of the room. Giant flower arrangements crowded in from the left and right. Now, 3 ½ hours after the wake had begun, the end of the line of mourners, friends and acquaintances was in sight. As the last one approached to pay her final respects, the reverend visited the line of family members in the front row, slowly walked to the front, and turned to the quiet crowd.

"We welcome you all here this evening to say farewell to Cyril Mark James. It is wonderful to see so many people – family, friends, business associates, and members of the extended community here this evening. Cy's family, his loving wife of 42 years, Melissa, his son, Thomas, his daughters, Anne and Shannon, whom I know Cy was so proud of, and his four grandchildren, all thank you for coming."

The reverend went on. "Since Cy's passing of natural causes in his sleep on Tuesday, I have talked with so many people about him. The stories they told me were all consistent. He was a loving family man, and a skilled and successful businessman. Cy was a great husband, a great father, and a great boss. His family will miss him dearly, and his employees will miss him as their leader."

"Would anyone like to speak?" the Reverend asked.

From the second row on the aisle, a man in his 60's arose and came to the front. He began, "It is not so sad to celebrate the life of a man such as Cy. He lived a full and successful life. As you know, I worked with him as the vice president of the company for 23 years. I know that Cy was a man of integrity. He loved his work and his family. People talk of Cy as a success. But we forget it wasn't always that way."

The man really wanted to make sure his audience understood. "Cy grew up in a poor family, as most families were in the 1940's. He had no role models for achievement. But he figured it out along the way. He often told me how much he had to learn to make the company work. How many obstacles he had to overcome to thrive and, sometimes, just to survive."

"If Cy were here, I know he'd tell you that he wasn't a 'natural.' He had a desire to build something great and to win, and he was determined to do what was necessary to accomplish that. He had a zest for life. I know Cy would tell you not to cry for him, for he lived life to the fullest. His only regret in dying would be that he would miss his family until he saw them again in heaven."

The man choked up, and stopped speaking for a minute. When he could, he got more words out. "I can't tell you what Cy has done for me and my family since I met him by chance 27 years ago. And so many other employees would say the same thing."

It seemed the man had more to say, but he cut it short; he could no longer control his voice. "We will all miss him."

Several other people came up to say things about the man who had been their loved one or boss. After listening to the speakers, everyone there knew that Cy had been a good man, even a great man. People from outside of his family and company – even those who had never really known Cy - wished they had. "What did he do to make people say such nice things about him?" some wondered. They'll never know now.

A soft, white mist surrounded Cy as he slowly regained consciousness. He wasn't confused, and he felt calm as he began to awaken and realize where he was. The white mist gave way to rich blues, and wisps of white and golden light. Cy felt a calm, because he knew he was going home.

Suddenly, he felt as if he stopped moving, though there was no landmark to indicate that he had. Before him, a white form appeared. Cy squinted to make out an angelic figure that became clearer as the moments went by. It was beautiful, Cy thought. He realized that that was his first clear thought since he had gone to bed Monday night.

The angel became firm and purposeful. She held up her hand to Cy and said, "You cannot come in." Cy's eyes widened. His mind began to race as he reflected over his life. "Why not?" He began to tremble. "What did I do? Haven't I been good?" The vision of the angel began to fade. "Wait! Wait!" Cy began to panic as he felt a sensation of moving backwards. The angel had nearly disappeared.

"What did I do?" Cy pleaded desperately. "No! No!" He felt the sensation of falling backwards. He heard the angel's voice in a distant whisper. "Your work is not done."

"What? What?" he yelled, trembling in panic. He fell down through space, tumbling, the sound of wind rushing loudly by. "No! Please!" He fell for what seemed like forever, and then he lost consciousness.

Chapter 2

New Work to be Done

Before he opened his eyes, he could smell it. For a moment he didn't want to open his eyes, for fear of what he'd see. It sure seemed very warm here, but not as hot as he had imagined. That smell, though. He wanted to gag.

Curiosity got him, and he slowly opened his eyes. He saw green. There was a written message. "For a good time call…"

"What! This is some version of hell!" Cy did a double-take to the left and right. "I'm in a Porta-Potty!" Now, taking control of all the faculties he had when he was alive, he instinctively kicked the door open. He was surprised to find he wasn't held captive, when it flung all the way open. The door came back on its spring so fast he had to stop it before it knocked him in the face. He stepped out to the side yard of an old home under renovation.

"What? Where am I?" Cy said bewildered. He stood in front of the Porta-Potty trying to make sense of it all. "Am I alive again?"

About 20 feet in front of him, a man came around the corner murmuring, "This job sucks." The man sat down on an overturned bucket near the bushes next to the house, and pulled out a small bottle in a brown bag to take a sip. Cy waited for the man to take notice of him, but he never did.

Cy thought, "If I'm alive again, then I want to go see my wife and tell her I'm here." He walked toward the street. "But where am I?" As he approached, he saw a sign on a truck. "Troy Builders." Cy recognized the area code as the same as his own. He grew excited and began to hurry. But when he got to the curb, he was stopped, as though by an invisible wall. He tried again, but he couldn't push across it. "What the..?"

A voice whispered to him. "Stay."

"Stay?" he repeated back. "Why?" Cy nearly asked, "Who are you?" But he stopped himself. He recognized the voice as the angel's. "What did I do? Why won't you take me? What did I do?" He stood still and silent, waiting for an answer. Nothing. He tried to cross the curb again, but still he couldn't.

"Stay," the voice whispered.

Cy thought, "If I'm alive, I'm sure not in control." As he pondered all this, confused, a rumbling noise began behind him. It got louder and faster, and a voice began to yell from the roof. Cy whirled around as the voice became a scream. "Heads up! Heads up! Heads up! Watch out!" Suddenly, a 90-pound bundle of roof shingles slid off the side of the roof. As it hit, it crushed a patio chair with authority, and was deflected enough to hit a glass patio door as it broke open, shattering the glass.

A woman screamed from inside and marched out of her front door seconds later, yelling. She was partly angry, but mostly scared. The worker who was shingling the roof raced down the ladder. The man who was sitting on the bucket was up now and acting defensive, saying he had nothing to do with it. Another man, a young man, appeared and looked at the broken glass, not knowing what to say.

The roofer started to apologize just as the woman let him have it. "My dog lies in front of the door! You nearly killed her!" The woman held a small dog in her arms, and she began to cry, still yelling.

Cy found himself closer to the scene, but nobody seemed to notice him. Just then, in the middle of all the drama, a loud truck approached. It was a concrete mixer. As intense as the scene was, the giant, loud truck helped to break things up. The woman turned, still upset, and went back in her house. The man on the bucket walked around the house and disappeared, and the roofer went back up on the roof.

The young man was left, looking at the truck. He looked at his watch, then looked up, not knowing what to do. The concrete truck driver waved him over. The young man walked to the street. Cy noticed that the young man wasn't affected by the invisible fence as he crossed the curb.

The driver spoke to the young man as if daring him to argue. "C'mon, I gotta' get this stuff outta' here quick," he said, motioning to the back of the truck. "Where do you want it?" The young man looked nervously at his watch again. He looked towards the driveway, towards the truck, and then back at the driveway.

"Well?" the driver barked impatiently. "There's footings we got formed in the backyard," the young man finally said, tentatively.

The driver quickly produced a paper and hung his arm out the cab window with a pen. "Sign your life away," he said, both sarcastically and routinely. The young man didn't know what the paper said, but he'd seen other men sign these papers before from a distance. He started to read the paper, but as he did so the driver slapped the side of the door with his palm and then turned it up, obviously annoyed. The driver certainly was not going to give the young man time to read it, so he just scribbled his name and handed it back to the driver. "Print your name, too," the driver said. The young man complied.

The driver said, "You got help, right?" The young man hesitated. "You got help, right?"

The young man steeled himself, and admitted loudly over the noise of the truck, "They aren't here yet, so I'm it right now. But they should be here soon."

"Jesus," the driver said, as if the wheels of industry had just been threatened. "Whatever," he said sarcastically. "So pull in the driveway?"

"Yeah," said the young man. "Pull right in here." He motioned with his hands, and looked like he was trying his best to do something he had never done before.

The young man walked back in the driveway, motioning the truck to come his way. As the truck pulled past the broken glass door, and its noise reverberated through the house, the woman looked out in terror. The driver saw the broken glass, and shook his head as he edged by with his giant truck. When he saw the footing forms in the backyard, he stopped the truck and motioned for the young man to come to the door.

The driver yelled, "You ain't gonna reach those forms from this driveway. You gotta' chute?" The young man didn't really know what a chute was, but he knew he didn't have one. "No," he said, now seemingly at the mercy of the driver.

"Well, we gotta pull up on the grass," said the driver.

"Okay," the young man said.

"It's gonna make ruts," the driver warned, directing the young man's next response with a shrug and lifted eyebrows, as if to say, "We have no choice."

The young man thought for a moment, then said, "Well, that's okay." He envisioned himself flattening the ruts with his feet or a rake that he had on site.

The driver revved the big diesel engine, shifted gears, and lurched the giant truck onto the grass. The young man was in front of the truck, waving the driver towards him. The heavy monster edged forward and downward as it sank deeper and deeper into the lawn. A sprinkler head popped out of the ground like a zit. The driver finally stopped, got out and slammed the door. "Damn!" he yelled.

The homeowner watched the scene from her window.

The young man knew that work would be needed to repair the lawn. He worried, as his mind raced. He looked at his watch again, then barked up and tried to reason with the driver. "Look, the damage is done, we can't change that. But if you pull up four feet more, we can at least fill these forms and unload your truck."

As the drama unfolded, nobody noticed Cy as he moved around the scene. Cy could see that the young man was trying his best — trying to salvage something good out of a bad situation.

The driver climbed back up into his smoking beast, with its giant drum revolving and its perishable load scratching inside to get out. The driver put the truck in gear, revved the engine, and let the clutch out. The truck moved forward two more feet, and then the unexpected happened. They both heard a dull thud as the truck suddenly dropped about 18 inches in the front driver's corner. "Oh frig!" the driver yelled. The young man wanted to just run away, like he had had nothing to do with it, but he realized that wasn't an option.

Just then a pickup truck marked "Troy Builders" pulled up with two men inside. They parked crooked in the street and ran towards the truck, which they could see from the street was listing over in the backyard. The young man watched them approach, half relieved and half scared of what they were going to say. "Holy crap!" the senior man said as he neared the truck.

"Freddie, where were you?" the young man yelled out to him. "You were supposed to be here 15 minutes ago! I tried my best!" He showed great worry.

"I know, Danny. It's okay. We'll figure it out." Now, at least, Cy knew the young man's name. It was Danny, and he appeared to be comforted by Freddie's statement.

Then Freddie added, "Troy will be here any minute." This statement took away Danny's comfort.

“Oh man, I’m dead,” Danny said.

Freddie got down on his knees and looked closely at the tire, which was buried up to its axle in the lawn. “It’s a septic tank!” The four men all cursed different words at the same time. Cy looked up to see the woman run inside her house. Cy knew she was probably calling her husband. Taking control, Freddie said to the driver, “Call a big ass tow truck to pull you out. By the time he gets here we’ll have you unloaded.” He said to his co-worker, “Jim, get the chute!”

Just then a shiny, new, extended cab pickup truck pulled up. A medium-built man in his thirties got out and immediately began surveying the situation. As he walked along the driveway, his eyes widened, his body became tense, and his forehead and neck contorted. The homeowner began to yell at him through the broken glass. The man from the bucket emerged, to say he had nothing to do with it. The driver began to reprimand him for not having capable people on site, and “there better not be any damage” to his truck.

This man in his thirties was the owner of the company working on the house. “Troy, it’s the septic tank. I got a tow truck coming and we’re going to offload the truck right now,” Freddie said, without waiting for a break in the yelling from the driver or the homeowner. Then Freddie turned away quickly and went to work.

Troy listened as the driver blamed it all on Danny. He listened to the horrified homeowner tell about the shingles, the door, her dog, the ruts, the septic tank, and who was going to pay for it, and could she use the toilet? And how long would it take to fix? How will the truck get out? And is the asphalt driveway damaged, too? She had called her insurance company and her husband…. it went on and on.

Troy tried to keep his wits, but Cy could tell he was stressed and becoming overwhelmed.

Cy knew enough about running a business to know that the cash register in Troy's head was totaling the damage, and emptying fast. Troy looked like he was going to blow.

Danny stayed silent, waiting, knowing what must be coming. He hoped the homeowner would not go inside; she was a buffer against Troy's anger toward him. He knew Troy to be pretty fair, and a pretty even-spirited guy in the three months since Danny had taken the job. But he also knew Troy was under a lot of pressure; he had seen Troy lose control once before.

Cy watched Troy endure the verbal wrath of his customer, and then promise he'd make it right. "Yes, Mrs. Kaspian…" But there was something about taking abuse from a person for someone else's mistake that could make a caring man pop. Self-control under pressure was a learned skill; Troy, while he always tried, did not have this one mastered consistently. Still unsatisfied, the homeowner finally went inside. Troy then turned towards Danny and closed in on him.

"You stupid idiot!" Troy began, "What were you thinking? Do you know how much a loaded concrete truck weighs?" Troy's voice grew louder as the frustration of both the day, and the whole week, swelled up in him and came out in an eruption. "This is going to cost me BIG. In fact, we'll have to work this entire job, and the next one, and the one after that, to give this customer a new septic tank, and then we STILL only break even! But do you care? No! Because you're stupid, that's why!"

The homeowner was back outside, witnessing the drubbing that Danny was taking in front of the driver, Freddie, Jim and herself. She felt bad for Danny. Freddie did too, but after working with Troy for nine years, he knew not to interrupt now. It wasn't often that Troy blew up. When he did, you didn't try to stop him.

After Troy hit his peak, and began coming down the other side, he turned to Freddie. "And where the hell were you?"

Troy almost retracted his question as soon as he asked it. Troy knew Freddie to be a skilled and loyal employee with good judgment — one he would have a hard time replacing. Freddie looked up from dragging the concrete out of the chute with a shovel and said, without emotion, "I was at the Dingman job this morning, where you wanted me to unload the lumber in the right spot — just like you told me to do before I came over here. The truck was late and Mr. Dingman had a lot of questions. I got here as fast as I could, but I was a few minutes late."

With that, Troy stopped his tirade. He stood there for a long minute. Everyone could see his anger turn to sadness. Troy realized it was his own fault. Last night he did ask Freddie to go to Dingmans. At the time, Freddie reminded him that they had a concrete truck coming at 10 a.m. But Troy told him to go anyway. He also had a talk with his people about the new job that was starting, and how Mr. Dingman was a nervous customer. Troy said that Mr. Dingman had a lot of influence in the community, and he should be shown special attention. So Freddie did what he was told. No one had told Danny what to do if the truck arrived before they did.

Freddie also didn't think it was a good time to tell Troy that a subcontractor had come to that same job site yesterday, looking for Troy, wanting his money, and telling everyone on site how he hadn't been paid yet. He also didn't want to tell Troy that the skylight they had ordered had come in the wrong size after a 2-week wait, or that the roofer's helper quit and the roofer wouldn't be done on time. All that would have to wait.

Cy observed a sad scene before him. An angry homeowner, calmed only by pity for another soul. A shaken foreman and helper, trying to pour the concrete before it set. An angry driver, who could only think about his own situation. A rattled young man, Danny, who stood there nearly motionless, stricken with rejection and embarrassment when he was only trying to help. Cy saw that even the roofer sat at the edge of the gable end, watching the scene, no doubt glad he was up there unnoticed.

Finally, Troy's thoughts turned inward. He was embarrassed by his own yelling, especially at Danny. He knew that Danny didn't deserve it. Just then Troy looked up at Cy. Cy was taken aback. It was the first time anyone had acknowledged Cy's presence. In fact, since he emerged from the outhouse, things had been happening so fast that Cy had forgotten he was on some strange mission that he didn't understand.

But before Cy could think about it too much, he heard a voice. He thought it must be the angel's voice again, but the angel's voice had been female, and came through his head. This voice was audible, and it came though his ears. It was Troy's voice. Cy looked at Troy, but Troy had already turned away.

"Great. Nosy neighbors. He's probably going to tell 50 people about this one. My name is mud in this town." Cy was sure it was Troy's voice he heard, but he could see Troy's mouth and it wasn't moving. "A new slider, that's $800, new septic tank, that's gonna be about two grand, plus landscaping, sprinklers, labor… so that's four grand – I'm screwed."

Troy could see Cy, although nobody else seemed to be able to. And Cy could hear Troy's thoughts.

"I don't get it," Cy said to himself. "What did I do? I was good. What did I do?"

"It's what you *didn't* do," a female voice inside his head replied.

"What? What didn't I do?" he queried. "What didn't I do?" But the voice was gone.

"Why was I on this job site? What didn't I do? I don't get it. Please, just…"

Chapter 3

An Awkward Introduction

Cy "woke up" again. He was startled. He looked around to assess where he was — sitting in a booth in a coffee shop. It was a blue collar sort of place. He slid towards the outside of the booth to get up, but when he reached the end of the seat, he was stopped. He rotated his hips towards the aisle, but he felt another invisible fence. "I have no control over where I go," Cy said in amazement, as he looked down, up, and around.

In front of him sat a paper cup with a plastic lid on it, with the near edge pulled up and torn off. He wondered if it was his or someone else's; but there was nobody else at his booth, and no one looked puzzled as to why he was sitting in their seat. He reached up slowly and wrapped his hand around the cup. It was warm.

"Do dead people drink coffee?" Cy wondered. "Am I dead? Am I alive?" Cy brought the cup to his lips and slowly tipped it back. It was good and perfect. The best sip of coffee he ever had. "Dead people don't drink coffee so I must be…"

Just then a loud man walked in with three other guys. They wore matching black t-shirts that read "Spider's Landscaping." Each man had plenty of tattoos, and each acted like he owned the place. All four walked up to the counter and barked their orders at a small man behind the counter. As they waited, they were loud and obnoxious.

Cy watched another truck pull up into the lot, which was strewn with trucks of all sizes, occasionally separated by a car or two. This truck he recognized. Troy stepped out of his truck and walked into the shop. He approached the counter, and seemed very comfortable in the place - until he saw the black t-shirts.

"Troy Becker, heyyy buddy," the leader of the group called to Troy, in a way that suggested Troy was no buddy of his at all.

"I heard you really screwed yourself yesterday!" He talked loud, so everyone in the place could hear him.

"Hi Billy, how ya' doin,'" Troy said softly, hoping to lead the jerk to lower his voice.

Billy continued. "Losing a concrete truck in a septic tank! Nearly killing the customer's dog with shards of glass. Holy crap, dude, you got problems!" Now everyone in the place was looking and listening.

"It wasn't like that," Troy said, pretending not to be bothered.

"That's not what I heard," Billy said, still talking loud. "Hey, thanks, by the way. Danny came to me last night for a job. He's a good kid and I'll put him to good use because I'm expanding to my fifth crew. When you downsize more, let me know, okay?"

Troy was shocked. He didn't know yet that Danny had quit. Danny was a good kid, and even though he made a mistake, Troy didn't want to lose him. Troy had plans to sincerely apologize for embarrassing Danny yesterday, but now he might never get the chance.

"Don't worry, Billy. We're good," Troy said.

"I hope so," Billy said, like a father who was wrapping up a lecture to his son. "You've been in business for 12 years and I wouldn't want the hammer to finally drop on you," he said, insincere as he could be.

"I hate that guy," Troy murmured to the man behind the counter, so Billy couldn't hear him. "Me too," he replied.

As the black shirts got their coffee, they filed out behind Billy. Troy turned to look and saw their black landscaping trucks. Cy heard Troy think: "Go mow your grass lawn, boy. That's all you know how to do."

Then Troy saw something that deflated him even more. It was Danny — leaning against one of the trucks, wearing a black t-shirt. Looking out of place, Danny got in the truck with two others, and they roared off, sounding like they had removed their mufflers on purpose. "Another good kid gone to the wrong side of the tracks. And I sent him there." Troy looked down at the floor and shook his head.

Troy hardly ever sat down at the coffee shop. He preferred to take his "bacon, double egg and cheese" and his medium coffee to go, since he was always running around. But today he had no motivation. "Thanks, Chris," Troy said, as Chris slid his sandwich across the counter in its translucent wax paper.

"No problem, buddy. You take it easy, alright?" Chris said, like he meant it.

"Yep." Troy walked to the booth across the aisle from Cy and plopped down. He opened his sandwich and slowly took a bite, gazing forward into space and chewing like he couldn't taste a thing.

Cy watched Troy. Somehow, Cy could relate to Troy, as if he had known him many years, and he felt in himself a caring for the man who was about half his age. Then Cy heard a voice. He thought it would be another one of Troy's thoughts that he'd been hearing. But it was the angel again.

"Your work is not done," the voice whispered inside his head.

"What?" Cy said softly, so he didn't get Troy's attention. "What? My work is not done?" Cy was learning not to ask the angel questions, because she never answered him. He thought about why he was here. "It's what I didn't do? Stay? My work is not done?" Cy tried to put the pieces together. He desperately wanted to understand why he was here. Would he ever get to eternal rest? "I keep being put in front of this kid, and I can't get away." Cy quizzed himself. "Wait a minute." Then it struck him.

Cy became aware of the shop again. He looked to his side to see Troy crumpling up the paper from his sandwich in a tight ball, and turn to get up from the booth. "Wait!" Cy said, not knowing what else to say. It was the first time he had spoken to someone else since he'd been "back." Cy waited to see if Troy would respond. Could Troy see him?

Troy looked at Cy abruptly. He stared and furrowed his eyebrows. "Uh-oh," Cy thought. "What do I look like? I'm freaking him out!"

"You lived the nightmare yesterday," Troy said.

Cy's eyes widened as he thought, "How did he know I couldn't go in? How did he know what happen..."

"You're Kaspian's neighbor," Troy said. "You saw the whole nightmare, right?"

"Oh, *that* nightmare," Cy said, relieved. "Uhh, no. I mean, yeah. I mean, I saw it yesterday. It was me, but I'm not the neighbor."

"Well, I hope you're not from OSHA," Troy said, with a trace of comedy peaking through the despondence in his voice.

"No, I'm here to help you," Cy said slowly.

"Funny, that's just what the guy from OSHA said last year," Troy replied. "I'll see you later."

"Wait. I'm here to help you," Cy said again, unable to figure out what else to say quickly enough.

"Yeah," Troy said slowly, trying to size up this odd statement from the stranger. "Are you from the government?" he asked, just to be polite and to keep the conversation going.

"No, not even close," Cy said.

"Well, who are you then?" Troy pressed.

"My name is Cy. I'm an ang…" He stopped himself. He scanned his mind. What would happen if he said that? Troy would think he's crazy.

"Okay Cy, well, I gotta go." Troy went to get up a third time.

"I'm an angel," Cy quipped, without thinking much more about what to call himself.

Troy stopped as he stood fully upright. After five seconds of staring down at Cy, he said, "Pleased to meet you, Cy the angel. I'm Troy the Easter Bunny. Maybe you ought to hit Chris up for another cup of coffee." Troy went for the door.

"But wait!"

Troy ignored Cy this time, and bound out the door.

"What the…" Cy thought, and then began talking to himself. "I can't believe… I'm not the angel; she is. What am I, then? I can't help him… He won't listen to me now. How am I gonna… "

Minutes went by and Cy heard a voice. It was his angel.

She whispered, "Give your gift."

Chapter 4

Man Interrupted

Cy appeared in a darkened room. "Where am I now?" he wondered. There was enough light from LEDs and a dim light coming through a window in a door to see across the small room. He walked carefully towards the door, felt the wall for a light switch, and flipped it up. The lights came on and he could see he was in a somewhat cluttered office.

There were stacks of files, papers and mail on an old metal desk. On the top of the pile sat an envelope ripped open; a collection notice crowned the stack. There were rolls of dusty blueprints filling a corner, along with battery chargers and a half-full cup of cold coffee. The message light on the phone desk blinked, and its digital display said there were 27 messages. On the wall near the door was a photo of an old weathered house, and just next to it was a photo of what looked to be the same house, completely transformed and new looking. On the wall over the desk there were photos of a pretty woman holding a baby.

By now Cy knew he was here for a reason. He looked at more of the framed photos hanging from the wall and, as he suspected, they were pictures were of Troy and his family. There was his wife, along with an attentive young boy leaning against Troy's leg, the cutest little girl in his arms, and a roly-poly baby in his wife's arms. Cy swallowed. It was the same combination as his own children, and memories began to flood back. "How short life is, and how precious," Cy whispered to himself. His eyes began to well up as he stared at Troy's family.

Just then Cy heard a truck pull up, and he saw the glow of headlights filter through the small building. "Oh no, he's going to think I'm a burglar." Cy swatted the light switch down and stepped out into the hallway. There was another office across the hall, and he ducked in. He heard keys in the nearby front door. Troy walked in with a purpose. He seemed in a hurry as he went into his office and turned the light on.

First Troy made a phone call. "Hi honey. Yeah, I'm at the office. I'll be home in 20 minutes, okay? Well, tell her I will, just as soon as I get home. Okay? Yes I will. I promise. Okay, I love you. Tell the kids Daddy loves them. What's she doing? Watching TV? What's monkey boy doing? Yeah, on his computer? Okay, lemme go and do what I gotta' do so I can get home. Bye, baby."

For the next two hours, Cy stayed silent as he listened to and spied on Troy returning phone calls, opening mail, and scribbling notes. At times Troy sighed. At times he laughed, and at times he cursed. Cy thought, "He really needs help."

Finally, when a digital clock glowed 10:07 p.m., Troy got up to leave. Cy panicked. Was he coming in here? Would he discover him? How will he get out? As Troy ran his fingers through his hair and let out a long breath, he exited his office and took a right. Cy could hear that he was in the bathroom. Cy acted fast; he slipped out of the office and sneaked out the front door.

Sixty seconds later, Cy could see the lights go off inside. Troy came out and faced the door to lock it with his key. As Troy turned, he saw Cy standing next to his truck, with the pinkish light from thc parking lot lamp shining down on him. Troy was startled and he paused. He wasn't afraid, as Cy was not a menacing figure. He nearly said, "Well, if it isn't my angel." But he was too tired, and not in the mood for comedy.

"Hello," Cy said.

"Who are you, and what do you want?" Troy said directly.

"My name is Cy."

"Yeah, I got that," Troy shot back, showing his annoyance. "What do you want?"

"I want to help you," Cy said.

Troy said coldly, "I'm not hiring, and if you wanted a job, ten o'clock at night is not the time to come ask for one." Cy could tell that he was in trouble, and at risk of never getting Troy to listen.

"Listen, I am not looking for a job, and I don't want anything from you at all. I was sent here to help you."

"Help me with what?" Troy said sarcastically.

"Your business. Your business and your life," Cy said firmly.

Troy paused. "I don't need your help," he said. "And who sent you?"

Cy thought of what to say. He knew he couldn't tell the truth because he'd lose him. "Someone who loves you," Cy said.

"Whaaaat? You're crazy. Who?" Troy's face matched the tone of his words.

"It doesn't matter right now. I am here to help you, and I *have* to help you," Cy said.

"How?" Troy asked, challenging Cy.

"I can help you accomplish your goals and have a better life," Cy said.

"My life is fine, and I don't need your help," Troy said, taking a step toward his truck.

"Look, I know it's strange, me showing up like this. But I know that you need help."

"You don't know nothin'!" Troy lashed out.

Now Cy felt himself come alive. He hadn't had an easy time in the school of hard knocks. As a young man he once thought he knew it all himself. And even when he did realize he needed help, there was a time when he was too proud to admit it – especially to strangers. Negotiating his own journey, he'd had his share of difficult people to deal with, and he knew how to handle this one. Skills and determination that he hadn't used in some time became available to him at this moment.

"I know a lot about you," Cy said.

"What do you know?" Troy said, in a direct challenge.

Cy looked directly in Troy's eyes without blinking. "I know you are a good man; otherwise I wouldn't be here. I know you've been in business for 12 years and you aren't making any money. I know you aren't happy and you want it to be better."

Cy pushed his words onto Troy. Troy tried to resist, but Cy continued. "I know you're trying your best. You work 70 hours a week, but you're running fast in the wrong direction. You feel like a slave instead of being free."

"You want to be successful, right? Right?" By now, Cy was almost yelling. "Right?" He demanded an answer of Troy.

Troy couldn't help but answer. "Right!"

"Well, if you keep doing what you are doing the same way you've been doing it, then how the heck do you expect anything to change?" Cy paused and watched Troy, who was now stunned. "Young man, if you keep doing what you are doing you can't expect different results! Can you?" Cy said, demanding another answer. "Can you?"

"No," Troy said, almost scared.

"You have to do something different!" Cy belted at him.

"I don't have time to do something different!"

"That's crap," Cy retorted. "Any guy who is busted like you has the same amount of time as any billionaire. You are just doing the wrong things," Cy said.

In an ever quicker exchange, Troy yelled, "But I'm working my ass off now!"

"I can see that. How's that working for you?" Cy yelled back.

"You smart ass. It's hard!" Troy shot back.

"Well if it's hard, you're doing it wrong! I can help you!" Cy declared.

"I am doing everything I can now!" Troy yelled – and then his face cracked, like he was going to break down.

Cy paused before going on, his voice a bit lower. "It's not about what you DO; it's about how you THINK." Troy stared at him with wide eyes. Cy sensed he had a direct path inside Troy now. He lowered his voice more. "Freedom comes not when you solve all your problems, young man. Freedom comes when you realize you can't do it alone."

There was a long pause. Troy sniffled and looked away into the dark, setting his jaw. Cy stood firm in front of him for another long minute.

Troy took a deep breath, stood up straight and regained his composure. "Why should I listen to you?" he asked, more calmly now.

Cy replied, "You tell me. Why should you?" Troy stared quietly, not knowing what to say.

"You want to be successful, right?" Cy asked.

"Yeah," Troy admitted.

"You want to be respected, right?"

Troy was listening. "Yeah," he whispered.

"You want to be a good provider for your family, right?" Cy asked.

"Yeah." Troy welled up again.

"You want to be a good husband, right?"

Troy looked at his questioner, his whole body tense, but he didn't answer. "You want to be a good father, right?" Cy drilled. Anger rose in Troy's eyes. "Something's got to change!" Cy declared.

Troy's eyes now flashed anger. "Go to hell," he said, and he reached for the door handle behind Cy. He pulled the door open and it hit Cy in the back. Troy slammed the door, pulled his truck backwards without looking behind him, and sped off into the night. Cy stood under the light in the parking lot, knowing he was beginning to break through, and wondering how much more it would take.

Cy said to himself, "I just might go to hell if you don't give it up." He watched the taillights fade in the distance.

Troy slipped his shoes off on the porch, and walked quietly inside. As he passed the dimly lit kitchen, he saw it had been cleaned up. His dinner plate was wrapped with cellophane on the counter. He paused and stared at the plate. He stood there, thinking.

A crayon drawing was on the refrigerator. It was a picture of a pickup truck – blue, with a white sign on the side. Inside the truck was a stick man's head, but it wasn't smiling. The top of the page read, "Daddy." The page hit Troy like a cannonball in the chest. He wiped his tears and quietly walked up the stairs.

He visited his son's room first. There his son lay, silent, his forehead damp, and his hair mussed. Troy just looked at him for a minute, and listened to his breathing. "I missed another day, monkey boy." He cried silently.

Next he went into his daughters' room. They were each nestled in their beds — precious, sweet, and innocent. He kissed each one and cried. He cried and cried, tears dripping onto their blankets. He couldn't stop.

When he could, he took a deep breath and quietly left their room. He saw a lamp on in the bedroom as usual. He quietly ducked into the bathroom and used a wad of toilet paper to dry his face. He went into his bedroom slowly, with his hands buried deep in his pockets and his elbows straight. He saw his wife, asleep with a book on her chest. She was beautiful. He watched her sleep for a minute from the doorway, thinking.

He walked over to the bed and kissed her softly. She woke up. "I thought you were going to be home in 20 minutes," she said. Normally, he'd explain how he found important messages and mail on his desk, and he'd tell her about all the things he had to do. But not tonight.

"I'm sorry, honey. I'm so sorry," he said, sincere as could be.

She opened her eyes and looked at him. "The girls made you a special cupcake. It's in the fridge." He put his head on her chest and wept. "Are you okay?" she asked softly. Troy didn't answer. He didn't have to. She held him against her. Without looking up, he knew she was crying, too.

Troy couldn't sleep. He thought about what Cy had said to him. He knew Cy was right. Everything he said was right. But who was he? Troy wanted to succeed desperately, but should he let this stranger, who appears out of nowhere, into his life? But what if he *was* the answer?

There was no use trying to sleep. It was 2 a.m. and his mind would not rest. Troy got out of bed and put on sweatpants and a t-shirt. He went downstairs and outside onto the front porch. He looked up at the dark blue sky for a long while, thinking.

"Something to fight for?" Cy said. Troy looked to his left and saw Cy on the porch. He began to realize that Cy wasn't going away. "Are you ready?" Cy asked.

"Leave me alone," Troy said, as he headed for the front door, trying to run away.

"I can't," Cy said.

Troy closed the front door behind him. But he didn't sleep all night.

Chapter 5

The Lumberyard Encounter

Cy awoke to a new morning. He didn't know where he was, but he knew he had work to do – and he had questions. "I don't get it. Why am I here again? To give my gift? Hadn't I used my skills when I was alive? What didn't I do enough of?" He needed to know. "As weird as this must be for Troy, it's just as weird for me," he thought. He worked the questions over and over in his mind.

The next day was a new day for Troy. He was sleep deprived, but he somehow felt a new sense of purpose. He didn't do anything differently when he went to the office. But he felt he should, or could, do something different. But what? Or was it all a dream? If it was, it was a very effective dream.

His mind was in a different place as he drove down the road. He didn't know quite what he was thinking, but something was different inside of him. His cell phone rang. "If you're going to Barker's, the guys want to know if you can pick-up three 2 by 8 by 12's from Hannan's so they can finish framing the roof. They're short."

"Okay, Sandra," Troy said.

"Okay, thanks. Hey, are you okay?" his office manager asked.

"Yeah, yeah, yeah, I'm fine," Troy answered, trying to sound convincing.

"Okay, well, if you need anything or anything, just let me know," she said.

"Thanks a lot, Sandra," he said. "Okay, bye."

"Bye."

Troy walked into Hannan's Lumber, with a distant look. "Hey, Skip. I need 2 by 8 Doug fir, three twelves."

"That's it today, Troy?" the man behind the counter, Skip, asked.

"That's it," Troy said.

"Alright, I gotcha covered, my man. The guys are loading a truck over at the pine shed. You wanna' just go get 'em, Troy?"

"Yeah, no problem."

"You know where they are? They're all the way in the back corner, just past the 16's, all the way back," Skip told him.

"No problem," Troy said automatically.

"Alright, chief. You have a good day, alright?" he shouted, as Troy was already walking out.

"Yep," Troy said, without looking back.

Troy pulled his truck around to the back corner of the yard. He backed up to the pallet of 12's, grabbed one, and slid it into the back of his truck. When he turned around, he saw Cy. Troy froze. Cy didn't say a word, but his look to Troy said, "What's it going to be?"

Troy thought about how Cy was right — about how he wanted to be successful, respected, and a good provider. More than that, there were things he wanted to do but couldn't, because he had no money. There were people he wanted to help but couldn't, because he needed help himself. And he knew, as much as it hurt him, that he could never be a good husband and father if he had to work 70 hours a week. Soon his kids would be grown, and he will miss it; he could never forgive himself for that. All the feelings came rushing back, and he was filled with emotion. But this time he wasn't running away.

In what seemed like a magical moment, he walked right up to Cy, and with firm resolve he declared, "I'm ready."

"Are you sure? Because you weren't so sure yesterday," Cy said casually.

"I'm ready," Troy repeated.

"How do I know?" Cy asked.

"Because I'm telling you," Troy said, firmer than before.

"Do you really want a great life?" Cy asked directly.

"I want it!" Troy said.

"How bad?"

"Bad!"

"*How* bad?" The exchange grew quicker and louder.

"Real bad!"

"Real bad?"

"Yes, I want it real bad!"

"What are you willing to do for it?" Cy asked.

"Anything!" Troy said, now yelling.

"Anything?" Cy asked.

"Yes… I will do anything." Troy said.

"Even if it scares you?"

"Yes!" Troy said.

"What if you don't change? Wouldn't that be easier?"

"No! Then I'll have this crappy life forever. I will change!" Troy said, with as much resolve as he could communicate.

Cy looked him right in the eye. "Good. If you don't WANT to, then there is nothing I can do for you. That is lesson number one. You must want to change so badly you will do anything. The intensity of your desire will determine the power and force you put out to move toward your goals," he said. "Seems like you have desire."

"I always have," Troy said.

Cy looked away. "Well, we're not going to work on your business," he said.

"We're not?" Troy said.

"Nope," Cy said.

Troy felt tricked. "What do you mean?" he said, irritated.

Cy looked back at him and paused. "We're going to work on you first," Cy told him.

"Me?" Troy asked.

"Yes. You. You've called all the shots, right? So you are the one who caused your business to be the way it is," Cy said.

Troy explained, "Well, yeah I call most of the shots. But I have an office manager who deals with stuff. And the people I hired, well, they made some mistakes. And some customers are… "

Cy cut him off. “I need you to make a pledge right now.”

“What?” Troy asked, thirsty for the answer.

“I need to you to take full responsibility for everything you are and everything you will ever be. Few people ever do this. There are no excuses. When you make excuses you give your power away to other people. You are responsible. For everything. Period.”

There was a long pause. Troy looked at him, thinking hard about what he had said. Finally, Troy said, “Okay. I pledge, I will never make excuses. I am responsible.”

“Good,” Cy said.

They stood there amidst the piles of lumber. Troy had finally surrendered and was ready for Cy to help him. “What’s next?” Troy asked.

Cy thought, “I don’t know, I’ve never done this be..” Cy stopped. It hit him like a bolt.

“Why don’t I talk to you later?” Cy said.

“When?” Troy asked.

“I don’t know,” Cy said with a distant look.

“You don’t know?” Troy said.

Cy was getting a feeling he was learning to recognize. He had gotten it just before he disappeared, or fell asleep, or whatever it was that happened to him. He didn’t want to tell Troy that he had no control of when he appeared, where, or why, or when he disappeared. He was part of a bigger plan, and he didn’t understand how it worked himself.

"Just go," Cy said. "Don't worry, I'll be in touch." Troy didn't quite understand, but he nodded and got in his truck and pulled away.

Cy stood there, his mind working and searching. "I've never done this before," he said out loud, repeating what he had said to Troy. "That's it! That's why I am here! Because I've never helped anyone like this!" He rolled the thought over in his mind. "I helped my company, my employees, my family… myself. Wasn't that enough? I guess not." He tried to put it all together. "But if this was the plan, if this is what I was supposed to do, why didn't I do it when I was alive?"

Troy's truck pulled to the exit of the lumber yard. Skip walked across the lot and yelled to Troy. "Hey! I thought you needed 3 sticks!" Skip said.

"Yeah," Troy said, hardly paying attention.

Skip pointed to the back of Troy's truck. "But you only got one," he said.

Troy turned and looked. "Oh, oh yeah." Troy's truck pulled back to the rear corner of the lot. He looked for Cy, but he was gone.

Troy had a new energy. He didn't know what to do, but he was determined to do *something*. He felt a new power in him. It was the power of hope. He went through the day, and others could feel it from him. He knew that by the way they responded. He had a heightened sense of awareness of what he was doing, and what was going on around him. He wondered when he would see Cy again. "I don't even have his phone number," he puzzled. But it didn't matter to him then. Troy was already a changed man.

That night, Troy went home at 6 p.m. and ate dinner with his family. After tucking the kids in, he slept like a baby.

Chapter 6

The Lesson of Self

The next day, after getting the jobs started and knocking out other morning duties in a rush, Troy went to his office. He sat down and swiveled his chair around to grab the pile in his in-box. When he turned back around toward his desk, he was startled to see Cy, sitting in the guest chair across from his desk. "Where did you come from?" Troy said.

"Uhhh, well, don't worry about that. We need to have a conversation," Cy said.

Although Troy was excited about what Cy had brought up for him in the previous two days, he felt a little uncomfortable seeing him now, in the light of a new day, in Troy's own space.

"Okay," Troy said. "What about?"

"About you," Cy said.

"What about me?"

"You need to change." Cy declared.

"I need to change?"

"Yes," Cy went on. "You are causing all your problems." Cy could see a resistance building in Troy already. Troy took a deep breath and let it out.

"*I'm* causing all my problems?" Troy repeated, now starting to sound indignant.

"Yes, that's right. Failure is self-inflicted. And you need to change that. You need to cause all your success, instead," Cy said.

Troy retorted, “I built this business. I sold most of those jobs. They got done because of me. I employ 13 people and I sell $1.5 million of work a year. Do you think that happened by accident? I made it happen. And you’re telling me I caused all these problems?”

“Don’t defend what you have done. It makes it harder to change,” Cy said.

“I am defending it. I worked hard and I got things done,” Troy said.

“Well, you have two choices, Troy. You can accept how things are, or you can accept responsibility for changing them.”

“Are you calling me irresponsible?” Troy shot back.

“Don’t hear what I am *not* saying Troy,” Cy advised.

“Why don’t you just teach me how to make some money? I need to make money. Can you do that?” Troy said, half knowing he was out of line.

Cy leaned forward and focused intently on Troy. “You don’t have a money problem. Your money problem is the result of your thinking problem.”

With an incredulous look on his face, Troy looked away.

“Listen to me, Troy. All businesses are the result of leaders thinking – or lack of it. Your business is a reflection of your thoughts,” Cy said profoundly.

“You think I’m an idiot?” Troy snapped.

“As you go, your business goes. You need to get this,” Cy said firmly. “The story of your business is the story of you.” Troy was getting more and more upset.

Troy got up purposefully. He grabbed his cell phone off the desk and his bag off the floor. "I gotta' go." He walked around Cy's chair and went for the door.

"Well then, you're just like most people," Cy said.

Troy stopped in the doorway. "What?" he said sarcastically.

"Most people want to change their circumstances, but are unwilling to change themselves… and they remain bound," Cy told him. Troy walked out.

Troy's truck pulled up to the Fisk's Sunoco station. An older man walked out towards Troy's truck. "Hey, Troy," he said, with no enthusiasm.

"Hey, Bob. What's goin' on?" Troy asked.

"Same shit, different day," Bob said, like he meant it.

"Oh yeah?" Troy said.

"Yea. I can't get no good help. Ya' know, I been here 42 friggin' years. And it's the same bullshit. I gotta get here at 6 a.m., and I work 'till 8. I can't find anyone to run the place, and to open and close and lock-up. And then I get called in the middle of the night for the towing." Troy, who was out of the truck now, listened to Bob's story as he had many times before. The gas cap clinked on the side of the truck as it dangled from its tether.

All of a sudden Troy looked up, listening with great interest. Bob went on, with one hand on the gas pump, gazing down the street at nothing. "I gotta do the towing 'cause I don't make no money off gas. Naw, there ain't no money in pumpin' gas," he said, as he pumped Troy's gas.

Troy stared as Bob continued. "I got no time for myself. Ya' know, I can't do nothin'. My son, ahh, he's off doing whatever the hell he does, I don't know. My wife and I, we can't go nowhere. Last night I was out on 95 at 4 in the morning bringin' a Jeep in. A kid fell asleep or was probably drunk like most of 'em are when I get to 'em... stupid kid, and I get back at 5 and gotta be here to open up at 6." Troy looked at Bob's tired, weathered face.

Bob continued, "I'm tryin' to sell the place, but who the hell wants to trade places with me, ya' know?" He put the nozzle back on its cradle and gave Troy back his credit card. Bob let out a deep sigh and said sadly, "Don't do what I'm doin'. See ya."

"See ya," Troy said. Troy pulled his truck away. Half a block away he said aloud, "Thanks, Bob."

Troy pulled up to his office and walked in with a purpose. Sandra was at the front desk paying bills. "Back so soon?" she said.

"Yeah, I forgot something important." He paused and looked at her. "Hey… a guy didn't…" he said, pointing first down the hall at his office and then to the front door.

"What?" she said.

"Ahh, nothing, nothing." Troy didn't think he should tell anyone he had an advisor when he couldn't explain who the advisor was, or where he came from.

Troy stepped down the hall and turned into his office. To his relief, he saw Cy sitting in his guest chair, waiting for Troy to come back. Troy closed the door and looked at Cy. "Okay. You're right again," he admitted.

Picking right up where he had left off, Cy continued as if it was the same earlier conversation with Troy. "Most people won't change because of pride and ego. They think if they change, or follow another's advice, or challenge what they have done in any way, it makes them look bad. You can either worry about looking good, or you can be successful and be sitting pretty in the long run. Which is it, Troy?"

"I… I got it," Troy said sheepishly.

Cy wanted to make sure he understood. "This is big, Troy. The strong and the wise admit they have weaknesses. When you say 'I know,' your mind closes and you miss the valuable lesson. Success is not what you get, but what you become. It's learning from everywhere, and everyone, the successful and the unsuccessful. But you have to be open to learn at all times. In fact, you have to be more than open; you have to seek new information, new ideas, and new strategies proactively all the time."

Troy's head was bobbing up and down. "I was learning from the unsuccessful just 10 minutes ago," Troy declared.

"I know. That's why I waited for you to come back," Cy told him. "And about that. I can't help you if you run away again."

"I know, I know. I'm not like that. I don't run away. It's just… It won't happen again. I want to get better, I have to get better, and you're helping me. I can see that now," Troy said quickly, a bit embarrassed and wanting to change the subject.

Cy was satisfied with Troy's promise and he went on. "To grow your business you have to grow yourself. It's a never-ending process of personal development. When you get better, your business gets better. If you stop learning and growing, your business stops evolving into something better."

"Okay," Troy said, casually accepting what Cy was saying.

Cy knew Troy didn't yet get his point at the level he needed to, so he went on slowly and deliberately. "You cannot be successful without a full understanding of this. To achieve something you've never done, you must become someone you've never been. It's not about your business, it's about you." Troy had now stopped moving, and was perfectly still. His face showed that he was finally latching on to the idea.

Cy pressed on. "You have to get out of your comfort zone. Sometimes way out. It will be scary at times. It's not easy. And that's why so few people manage to achieve greatness in any endeavor. They become something smallish, and then spend the rest of their life living the same year, over and over, defending who they are." Troy was fixed on Cy's words. Cy said, "This is not for you, young man. If you are to achieve your true potential, then parts of the old Troy must die to let the new and better parts of the new Troy be born and live."

Troy was slowing nodding. Cy paused long to let Troy process the idea, then he went on. "Early in my career, I thought I knew what I needed to do to make my business flourish. But I got stuck. I was stuck for years, but I knew what to do. And I kept trying to do it, but it wasn't working. Then I met a wise man, for just a few minutes. He was talking about business when he said these words to me: 'The bottleneck is at the top of the bottle.' I never saw him again, but his words had a profound impact on me. My business was stuck — because I was."

"What did I make you promise in the lumberyard?" Cy asked.

"Uh, that I am responsible for everything that has and ever will happen around me," Troy said. Cy waited. "It's kind of the same thing," Troy said, making a connection.

"Right," Cy said, satisfied. "Let me ask you a question, Troy," he said, now sounding like he was changing the subject. Troy took a tall breath and let it out, getting ready for another idea. "Do you believe in yourself?"

Without hesitation, Troy said, "Absolutely. I have done a lot of things and I do more than most people I know, with my business and all."

"What do other people have to do with your believing in yourself?" Cy responded. Troy looked a little confused and felt another lesson coming his way.

"Well, I mean, I have this business, and I've run it for 12 years, and a lot of other guys I know tried but didn't make it, and I'm still here," Troy defended weakly.

"Both life and businesses are full of paradoxes. You should compare yourself to others to learn and gauge and understand. But you should never compare yourself to others so that you feel good about yourself. If your self-esteem is attached to doing better than others, you're going to have a big problem," the elder man said.

"Oh," was all Troy would say.

"There will always be people who are doing better than you. Are they better than you? Should you feel worse when you see them?" Cy probed.

"No," Troy said, knowing that answer.

"Well, then, why would you feel good when you are doing better than someone else?" Cy paused for Troy to consider his question. "And what if you lost it all? Would all your self-worth, self-esteem and self-belief go down the drain with your possessions?"

"I hope not," Troy said.

"When I ask you if you believe in yourself, and your abilities, I am not asking if you believe in what you have done compared to other people," Cy said. "Everyone has different talents and abilities and goals and desires. I am asking if you believe in your ability to realize your own potential; and that's not about what you have done. It's about what you accomplish compared to what you are *capable* of accomplishing, and nothing else. It's believing in what you can do that you have never done before. Do you understand?"

Cy was taking Troy deep, but the young man followed. "I understand. I do. I do believe in myself. I can do things I've never done before," Troy declared.

"You're going to need a heap of faith in yourself, young man." Cy looked at Troy as if to ask if he was ready.

"I can do it," Troy said. At that, Cy sat back up straight, away from Troy. They both breathed. Cy slowly broke a smile. Troy took another breath, and smiled back. They sat there for a minute, not saying anything.

Cy stood up and took a step toward Troy. When Troy looked up at him, Cy was holding a book. He handed it to Troy. It was a beautiful rich, blue, hardcover book. Troy stared at it, admiring the rich gold embossed pattern on the cover. Slowly, as if opening a great gift, he opened the book near the center of the pages. Troy was confused. It was empty. The pages were blank. He fanned the pages – they were all blank. He looked up at Cy – but Cy had vanished.

Troy stood and looked around his small office. The door never opened and there was nowhere to hide. He was drawn back to the book that he held in his hands. He closed it and looked at the cover again. The gold lines in the deep blue made a rich border with patterns in the middle. Troy was mesmerized by the cover, but confused by the blank pages inside. He opened the book again to page one. There, in beautiful script, were three words: "Capture the ideas."

Troy sat for a moment, and grabbed a pencil from his desk. He held it to the paper, and then suddenly threw it back and took a pen. He looked at it, and threw it back in the drawer. He reached way back and found a beautiful pen, still in its felt lined box, that he had gotten for Christmas from Karissa. He slowly and respectfully twisted it to life and began writing in the book. He wrote everything he could remember that Cy had said to him — even what Cy said before he believed him.

Troy wrote about taking responsibility, about not holding onto ego and pride, about seeking new ideas from everywhere, having the same time as a billionaire, and everything he could remember. He wrote about doing things differently, not making excuses, and believing in himself. After he wrote about letting the old Troy go, so the new Troy could emerge, he rustled through his desk to find a highlighter and he highlighted his words. He wrote in as much detail as he could, underlining and rewriting ideas and how he interpreted them. His mind was alive.

Once he emptied his thoughts and recollections onto the page, a new thought edged into his mind. It grew and worried him. "But WHAT do I do?" He sat there and stared at a blank spot on the wall and wondered what to do. He heard Sandra punch out and close the front door. He looked down at the pages in his book that were no longer blank and his eyes fell on one word – "Faith."

Troy noticed the digital clock in his office as its numbers changed in the new silence. It was 5:30 p.m. already. He stared at the numbers. He jumped up with the book and ran to his truck.

Troy wanted to buy a dozen roses but found only $12 in his pocket. He knew two out of three credit cards were maxed out, but he couldn't remember which two. He put the dozen roses back in the water bucket with the rest.

As he ran into the house at 6:02 p.m. he smelled dinner. It was the greatest smelling dinner ever. He heard the kids' voices, and the sound was beautiful. He stepped into the kitchen and heard three voices at once yell, "Daddy!"

With a single rose in his hand, he grabbed Karissa and wrapped his arms as far around her as he could, buried his face in her neck and hair, and hugged her tight. Two of the kids grabbed his legs. "We're going to make it work, baby," he whispered in her ear.

"Make what work?" she said, feeling his emotion.

He whispered back. "Everything."

Chapter 7

To the Future

It was a bright and fresh morning as Troy pulled into the coffee shop. As he walked in he saw many friendly faces. "Hey, Troy," one voice called.

"Morning, Phil." Phil was a self-employed carpenter whom Troy had known for more than 10 years. He was a good guy and a personal friend of Troy's. As Troy turned towards the counter he saw Teddy, his best friend. Troy had gone to high school with Teddy, and knew his family well.

"Hey Teddy! How's it going?" Troy said enthusiastically.

"Pretty good," Teddy replied. "How you doin'?"

"Ahh, good, really good," Troy said, giving a thoughtful response to an automatic question.

"Oh? What changed?" Teddy asked.

"Umm..." Troy wondered if he should try to explain how Cy had shown up, but he couldn't make sense of it himself. "Nothin'. Just feeling good today."

Teddy was a self-employed flooring and tile contractor. He struggled often, but he wasn't a complainer. That's why Troy and Teddy got along so well; they were both positive people, and inside, they wanted to do better.

"Morning, Chris," Troy said, as Chris called Troy's usual order into the microphone. Chris was the owner of the coffee shop. He, too, was working hard and long, trying his best, but Troy knew he was a slave to his business. Still, Chris loved it and made the most of his situation. Chris chatted with Troy for a moment like they often did. He was a smart guy. To Troy, he seemed almost too smart to be running a coffee shop. Troy always listened to Chris for a helpful piece of advice, whether it was about business or just about getting along.

Chris put Troy's coffee on the counter. Dark, one sugar. Troy took it and turned to sit with Teddy at the counter while he waited for his sandwich. Troy saw the black trucks pull up into his lot and park crooked, each one taking up three or four spaces with their trailers in tow. Two beer cans fell out of one truck as the mob made their way in.

The whole mood of the shop changed when they entered. People looked up, and Billy made sure they did so with his loud banter. After they ordered at the counter, they made their way to the nearest booth and seized it, like pirates taking a ship. Billy spoke loudly to the guys in the opposite booth so everyone in the shop could hear him. "I'm thinking of opening a remodeling company," he declared. "There's a market for it around here, and there's nobody doing quality work that people can rely on."

Billy glanced over at Troy to see if he heard him. He knew he did. Everyone in the place did.

Teddy turned back toward Troy, bowed his head down and whispered, "What an ass."

Both Troy and Teddy knew that Billy only knew how to cut grass. "How about you and me go take the five of them out right now?" Troy said, only half joking to the 160-pound Teddy.

"Nahh, I don't want to spill my coffee; it's just the right temperature," Teddy replied. "Yeah, you're right," Troy said, closing the matter.

Next, Troy visited the office and checked in with Sandra. Kara, a smart, eager college student, who was working part time in the office, was just getting in. Both Sandra and Kara had loads of questions for Troy. The mail, email, and bills for him to check were piling up. He made an effort to find some of the most urgent items and rush through them.

"Did Piper sell anything this week yet?" Troy asked.

"Nope," Sandra said, with an obvious disdain for Piper. Troy sucked his teeth.

Tom Piper was Troy's only salesman. He'd been working for Troy for eight years. First Piper was a carpenter, but he wasn't very good and he was painfully slow. Rather than bring himself to fire him, Troy tried him out as a salesman. Troy had been spending all his time estimating, and he needed someone to lighten the load. That was five years ago. Now Piper was part of the wallpaper at Troy Builders. He didn't sell much, but Troy didn't have time to find someone else. And who else could he get, anyway?

Then Troy was out the door and in his truck, on his way to one of the two larger jobs he had going on right now. On the seat by his side was the blue and gold book. Troy put his hand on the cover, and felt a fraction of the daily stress already building in him start to ease.

He toured the progress at Kaspian's house, and talked with Freddie. Freddie was his main man. He had a great attitude, could build anything, had common sense, and had a great work ethic. Troy's other employees and subcontractors alike listened to Freddie. Besides that, the customers liked him, too.

Troy made notes on what would be needed for the job each day for the next week, and went off to check the Dingman job.

Mr. Dingman had 15 minutes of questions, which led to a long list of items for Troy to check and answer. As Mr. Dingman went through his checklist for the day, Troy's blood turned cold. He realized he hadn't included the cost of a large stained glass window in the contract. Troy had waited for the quote from Hannan's, but he put the proposal together before getting it. "Damn," he thought. "We're just starting this job and I'm out two grand already," trying to hide his frustration from Mr. Dingman.

He spoke to his employees about concerns and details of the job. "Oh, a guy stopped by and wanted me to give this to you, Troy," said Howard, Troy's newest lead carpenter. From his nail pouch, Howard pulled out an envelope, now dusty with nail imprints in it. Troy opened it. It was an estimate and note from the cabinet and tile guy, who had underestimated the job verbally to Troy. Here was his written quote for an additional $1,457.

"You gotta' be... " Troy said out loud, shaking his head. The note also said that the guy couldn't start until 9 days after they were scheduled for him. Troy felt the tension build in his chest and neck.

Cy sat in the passenger seat of Troy's truck, rolling his own questions over in his mind. "Why didn't I 'give my gift' while I was here? Why was I hoarding my talent?"

While the situation was serious for Cy, he'd taken satisfaction in helping Troy so far. He looked forward to talking to him more.

Troy walked out to his truck as he completed a call to Sandra. To his surprise, he saw Cy in the truck. He grabbed the door handle and paused for a deep breath. He opened the door and forced a smile.

"Hi," Troy said, trying to shake off how his day was going.

"Let's go. We have work to do," Cy said, smiling.

Troy jumped in and backed out of Dingman's driveway. "Where are we going?" Troy asked, now a bit excited and anxious that Cy was here again.

Cy looked at Troy. "To the future."

Troy drove where Cy directed him. Troy looked like he was holding back a question. Finally, he let it out. "How long is this going to take?"

"Why?" Cy asked back.

"Well, I have a little time, but today is not the best time for …"

Cy interrupted. "There will never be a *best* time, and there will never be a *right* time, and you will never *find* time. If you are serious about your future, you must MAKE time."

Troy knew that Cy was right, and he was disappointed in himself that he even said such a thing. "So I am making time right now then, right?" Troy asked, wanting Cy to know he was on board.

"Yep," Cy asserted calmly, looking straight out the windshield.

They got out in a remote section of Beardsley Park. The sun was warm and the air was still. There was nobody else around. Cy walked over to a picnic table and sat down. Troy sat down opposite him, pen in his ear, and placed the blue book down on the rough surface. Cy smiled when he saw the journal. He was glad Troy knew to bring it.

"Now you are going to plan your future," Cy said.

"You mean like a business plan?" Troy asked.

Cy smiled as he fed out the next idea. "Let me ask you a question, Troy. If you were going to write a business plan on how you'd get there, where would the plan be getting you?"

"To success!" Troy said, proud of his answer, and hoping it was right.

“Where’s that?” Cy asked.

“Uh… well… to solve my problems… and… to fix my business so it works for me,” Troy thought out loud.

Cy lifted his eyebrows and made a face. Troy looked at him. His eyes shifted up and to the left, and to the right. His cell phone rang and interrupted them. Troy shut it off without looking. He knew Cy was onto something important for him already, and they had only just begun. “I’m not clear,” Troy said.

“I know,” Cy said. “And that’s what you need to do. Get clear.”

Cy went on. “A vision of what you want, exactly what you want, is what you need. It’s different than a business plan. A business plan is how you are going to get there. A vision is where you are going.”

“I get it,” Troy said. Troy was eager to work with Cy now, letting his resistance go. He had always wanted to live a wonderful life, and do so many things, and he knew Cy was here to help him. He had developed an appreciation for the old man, and he sensed that Cy’s presence was something special that he should take advantage of.

“Most people don’t plan their future. They live by chance. They let their life move by the circumstances that happen around them. They never decide what they want, and they wind up disappointed later that their life didn’t turn out better. This isn’t for you, Troy. You have to start living by choice,” Cy explained. Troy hung onto Cy’s words, because he knew they were right.

“Before you do it, you have to see it,” Cy said. The young man and the old man sat there at the picnic table. Sunlight filtered down through the trees.

“What should I see?” Troy asked.

"I can't tell you what to see," Cy replied. "It's not my vision. It's yours. You have to decide. It's unique to you. You must never try to live someone else's dream. Be uniquely you." Troy gave Cy short quick nods, telling Cy he knew what he was talking about. "If you don't know exactly where you are going, exactly what you are trying to do, then how can you get there? You see?" Cy said.

"I got it," Troy said. "But I thought I knew what I wanted before, and I just couldn't make it happen," he admitted. "It's not like you can just decide and do it." His eyes shifted to the side and his shoulders slumped a little.

"It's not?" Cy asked, looking right into Troy now. Troy processed the words.

"Okay, well, let's say it's that easy. How am I going to do it? I've been trying and trying hard for 12 years. How am I going to accomplish a goal just because I decide on it?" Troy asked.

Cy replied, "Don't worry about the *how* right now. How is not what we need to talk about today. Do you believe in yourself?"

Troy remembered the conversation they had had yesterday. "Yes," he said resolutely.

Cy nodded and smiled, telling Troy he had just answered the question of *how*.

Cy went on. "One thing's for sure, Troy. You can't bring a vision you don't have into reality. Right?" Troy paused and nodded, looking more confident. "Can you accomplish goals you don't have?" Cy asked.

"No," Troy responded.

"Can you exactly hit vague goals?"

Troy thought for a moment. "No. That's part of my problem. I want to be successful, but I really don't know exactly what I want. I mean, I have a lot of ideas, but they're scattered," he admitted.

"I know. Now you have to decide exactly what you want," Cy said.

"But even if I decide, I don't know how to…" Troy stopped himself.

"Would you please put the *how* aside for now?"

"Okay, okay, okay," Troy apologized. "I just haven't been too good at it so far."

"The past does not equal the future," Cy told him.

"Well, it would if I did the same things I always did," Troy said, proud of what he had learned from Cy already.

"Now you're getting it!" Cy said proudly. He added, "Old thoughts create old outcomes."

Troy was thinking the idea through. "But how do I know what my future should be, or... I mean, what I should decide to do," Troy questioned.

"You already know everything you need to know," Cy told him. "You can create whatever you want for your future. You just need to decide what it is." He waited as Troy sat thinking.

Cy asked, "For example, how much money do you want to make?"

"Well, I'm not making much now."

"You mean in the past?" Cy said.

"Yeah, I haven't made much money," Troy said.

"You can't change the past, can you?"

"No," Troy agreed.

"But you can change the future," Cy said, waiting for agreement.

"How?" Troy asked.

"By what you do in the present," Cy revealed. "You're changing your future right now."

"I can see that," Troy said, nodding and cracking a smile.

"So how much money do you want to make?" Cy asked.

"Umm, well, my best year I made $110,000. But I made $32,000 the year before, and broke even the year after, so you can't really count that," Troy thought out loud.

Cy's face turned angry. He stared at Troy and squinted. "The past is over!" Cy shot at him.

"I know," Troy said.

"So why do you keep talking about it?" Cy asked him tensely. Troy thought he had the concept down, but he realized he didn't. "The past has nothing to do with this conversation. You are going to create a new vision of what you want," Cy told him.

"Okay, $150,000!" Troy shot out.

Cy downshifted and looked at him, in partial disbelief. "What?" Cy said slowly.

Troy didn't know what he said that was wrong. This was all very uncomfortable for him. "$150,000?" he said, now turning it into a question.

"That's nice," Cy said, as he began to laugh. He couldn't help it. And once he started laughing he couldn't stop. He laughed harder and harder, trying to get the words "I'm sorry" out. Cy hunched over the picnic table bench sideways, trying to stop laughing, but to no avail.

"What the hell are you laughing at?" Troy said, irritated.

This just made Cy laugh more. Finally, he began to get control of himself. "Nothin', nothing,'" he said, with a huge smile on his face, wiping his eyes.

"Sounds like something to me!" Troy barked with a straight face.

"No, no… it's fine," Cy said, giggling the last of the humor out. "Look, young man. The only real limits you have on what you can achieve are the limits that you impose on your own thinking. You have to drop limited thoughts and replace them with unlimited ones instead."

"Unlimited? Okay, a billion dollars!" Troy said, his feelings still hurt from Cy laughing at him.

"Hey, I'm sorry for laughing. I couldn't help it," Cy said. He started laughing again. "You're right, it's not unlimited. I was trying to make a point to expand your thinking."

"What's wrong with $150,000?" Troy asked.

"Nothing. It's a start, I guess."

"Well then, what should it be?" Troy quipped.

"I can't tell you," Cy said.

"Well, give me an idea, then," Troy pleaded.

"Are there other companies in your industry that are bigger than you?" Cy asked, now sounding like he was getting down to business.

"Of course," Troy admitted.

"Well, how much are their sales a year?" Cy asked.

"Oh, there are some huge ones. I see in the trade magazines that there are $30 million companies around the country."

"Oh," Cy said, nodding, not surprised at all.

"The biggest one I know in my state is $12 million, but I know there must be bigger ones, too," Troy told him.

"Well, how much is an average profit margin in a well-functioning company, you think?" Cy asked.

Cy could see Troy's light bulb flash, as he thought for a moment. "10 percent?" Troy asked.

"Uh huh," was all Cy gave him. They were silent for half a minute as a green leaf fell gracefully onto the table between them.

"Okay, $150,000 is too low," Troy admitted.

"You bet it is. How much do you pay your highest paid employee?" Cy asked.

"With a bonus and the truck, I pay Freddie $98,000," Troy told him.

"Okay, so let's say $100,000. What's the least Freddie will make this year?"

"About $92,000," Troy said.

"So Freddie has no risk, right?"

"Right," Troy said.

Cy went on. "Who takes all the risk?"

"Me," Troy said.

"Who has all the responsibility?"

"Me," Troy said.

"Whose name and credit rating are on the line if things go bad?"

"Me," Troy repeated automatically.

"Who has to make all the pieces work?"

"Me."

"And you think that's only worth 50 percent more than Freddie makes — IF you can make it all work out?"

Troy thought about it. "Yeah, $150,000 is too low," he said.

"So how much do you want to make?"

"I can't just name a number," Troy said, his last resistance to the idea coming out of him.

"Why not?" Cy asked. "Life is a do-it-to-yourself project young man." He was done with Troy's hesitation. "I want you to open that book, and write down how much money you want to make. Then I want you to write down how many hours a week you want to work. Then I want you to write down as many reasons as you can why you want to accomplish this goal. Write down all the things you can have or do as a result, and all the things you can give or express as a result."

He stood up. “Got it?” Cy didn’t wait for Troy to respond; he turned and walked away into the park.

Troy watched for a bit as Cy walked away, then he turned and looked down at the book. The gold leaf design embossed into the cover glimmered in the sunlight. He opened the cover to read the words “Capture the ideas” again. He flipped past the pages he had already written on, to a fresh page. His pen descended towards the blank sheet. He wrote the number. His number. It was big, exciting and scary.

For an hour, Troy thought and wrote. He became engrossed in it, and excited about what he had committed to paper. He lost track of time as he remembered what Cy had asked him to do. As he finished writing another reason in a long list, he looked up. Cy was there holding a cardboard tray. “Lunch?”

“Thanks. Aren’t you going to eat?” Troy asked, when he saw that Cy didn’t get anything for himself.

“I don’t… I mean, I’m good. I got this coffee.”

Cy could see a new energy in Troy. Something had happened to him while he was away. But Cy had known it would happen.

“So what did you come up with?” Cy asked.

Troy flipped a few pages back in his book. He paused and crowed, “$600,000!”

Cy smiled wide. “There you go! So how did you wind up at $600,000?”

Troy explained confidently, “I’ve always had in my head that my business could do $5 million a year. It was a dream, really. I never wrote it down and didn’t think about it much, but I fantasized a few times. But I know I can do it. I don't know HOW. I just know I can," he said, looking up at his teacher, who smiled and nodded in approval.

Troy went on. "If I have a net profit of 12 percent, that equals $600,000. And it's as simple as that."

"Yes it is!" Cy said. Troy was excited!

"Okay, so how many hours a week are you going to work?" Cy asked.

"Fifty!" Troy said. "From 7:30 a.m. to 5:30 pm, five days a week, and off on Saturdays and Sundays."

"Very good!" Cy said. "Now how about your reasons?"

Troy turned the book to Cy, to let him read his long list. "Wow!" Cy said. "The more reasons you have, the better chance you'll accomplish your goals and overcome obstacles when they come. You sure have a lot of reasons."

Cy read his list, which included taking the family on vacations, attending school events with the kids, teaching Tarin how to fish, taking his girls out for tea in the city, paying off his mortgage, moving to a bigger home in the next town, and sending the kids to college.

He also knew he'd have to take care of his parents and Karissa's parents when they ran out of money in retirement. There were many reasons of all kinds on Troy's list. "I'm proud of you, Troy," Cy said, sliding the book back.

"Now I have a vision to step into," Troy said. He seemed relieved that this work was done.

"Well, you have part of it," Cy said.

“Part of it? No I’m clear. This is what I want to achieve,” he said to Cy with certainty.

“There’s more,” Cy explained. “What you have done so far is the personal goals part. But you can’t achieve those goals without your business. Your business is the vehicle that will get you there. So now you need to develop your vision of what your business is going to look like, in order to produce that much profit while you work 50 hours a week or less,” Cy explained.

Troy took a deep breath. He thought he was done for now. He sure felt exhausted. He didn’t know what his business would need to look like to produce that profit. He knew this wasn’t going to be easy, and he gave Cy a look that told him as much.

Cy saw Troy looking overwhelmed. “Thinking is the hardest work of all, Troy. That’s why so few do it,” Cy told him, trying to give him strength as he spoke. “Hear me, young man. You are no longer in the remodeling business. You are in the knowledge business. You are in the thinking business. And the quality of your business will be determined by the quality of your thoughts.”

Troy sat, transfixed on the words. He was beginning to get it.

Chapter 8

Designing the Machine

A sparrow landed on the end of the picnic table, inspecting the crumpled up hamburger wrapper and cardboard french fry boat on the table.

"You have to clearly create the business you want in your mind first," Cy told Troy. Troy sat up and held the pen in his hand, looking down at a new page in his journal.

Cy paused. "To be a visionary, you have to see things that aren't there yet, and believe in things that haven't happened yet. Let's start with what business you're in," Cy suggested.

"What do you mean? I'm in the remodeling business!" Troy quizzed back.

Cy explained, "That's too broad. In order to get really good at something, you have to specialize. Have you had the experience of some types of jobs going well, and others not going so well?"

"Absolutely," Troy responded, knowing exactly what Cy was talking about.

"And some you make money on, and some you don't. Right?"

"Right," Troy said.

"And some you're good at, and some you're not, right?"

"Right."

Cy slowed his voice. "And some work you love, and some work you hate, right?" He concluded his line of questioning.

Troy thought on this last question. "Yes, you got it. How did you know?"

"I've seen the movie before," Cy said. "Let's start there. In order for you to be happy, your company shouldn't be doing work you don't like to do. Does that make sense?"

"Totally," Troy agreed.

Cy continued. "There's another big reason to only do what you like to do. I'm going to take a guess, and say that the work you don't like was also the work that your company wasn't very good at – right?"

"Yeah. When I dreaded the job, I couldn't get excited about it," Troy said, scanning his memory as if remembering particular jobs.

Cy felt satisfaction as he led Troy through these thoughts, because he could see that he was helping Troy discover what he already knew, but could not yet see. "If you're going to make money doing a type of work for your customers, then you have to be good at it. And in order to be good at it, you have to have a passion for it. And when you have a passion for it, it doesn't seem so difficult. In fact, it could be fun!"

"Yea, I got that. I gotta' stop doing pools," Troy convinced himself.

"Pools?"

"Yeah, a few years ago I went to a class to learn how to do in-ground pools. I only did a couple a year, but I hated it and lost my shirt on every job," Troy told him.

"I want you to put a line down the middle of a sheet of paper. On one side write down all the types of work you like, and on the other, all the types of work you don't," Cy said.

After a few minutes, Troy looked up.

"Okay, what are you going to stop doing?"

Troy hesitated. “Well I can see a problem,” he said, as he looked down at the list.

“What’s that?” Cy asked.

“If I stop doing all this stuff, that’s almost half my business,” Troy said, sounding like it wasn’t going to work.

“Awww, don’t worry about that. That just means we have to get a lot more of the work you *do* want. We gotta’ get a lot more work anyway if you’re going to do $5 million – right?” Cy said, like it was no sweat.

“Yeah… yeah... ” Troy trailed off, not sounding convinced.

“So what are you going to stop doing?” Cy asked again.

Troy looked down at his list and read: “Pools, kitchens, baths, interior flooring, home theaters, and interior gut out remodel jobs.”

“What kind of work do you like to do, then?” Cy asked.

Troy read the other column on the page that he had drawn a happy face on top of. “Siding, windows, roofing, gutters, landscaping, driveways, sidewalks, decks, stone work, retaining walls and patios.”

“Well, it looks like you love to be outside, and don’t like the inside work very much,” Cy observed.

Troy looked at his list, scanning the columns again. “Yes! That’s right! I hate inside work!” Troy had an epiphany. “I hate working where people are living, and doing all the fine details, and worrying about colors and finishes. It’s just not my thing,” he said, looking like he had made a decision. He nodded his head with big up and down motions. “Man, I can’t wait to finish the last inside job,” he added, looking excited.

"Very good, young man. You've made a big step here. Most people try to work on their weaknesses, but it's far better to develop your strengths," Cy told him, satisfied with the outcome of the exercise.

Troy took it farther and declared, "I'm a home exterior specialist." He said it again. "A home exterior specialist." He wrote it in the book, liking the way the words sounded. Then Troy looked up at the horizon and pondered for a moment. He knew his future had just been changed.

The corner of the park was still quiet. A mother pushed a stroller in the distance. The sun had changed its position in the sky, and beams of light slid in sideways towards the picnic table under the trees.

Cy said, "Do you have a calculator?"

"I do, right here on my iPhone," Troy said, reaching to his side.

"Okay, what's the average size job for the exterior work you do?" Cy asked.

"Uhhh, about $18,000. I mean some jobs are $5,000, and I've done some $80,000 jobs; but I'd say around $18,000 might be the average," Troy said.

"Okay, if you are going to make a $600,000 profit on $5 million worth of work, how many exterior jobs do you need to sell and complete?" Cy asked, making perfect sense to Troy.

"Uh, okay, well that's $5 million divided by $18,000, which equals 277.77… call it 278 jobs," Troy said proudly. Suddenly he stopped, his face showing despair. He paused and thought about trying to handle 278 customers. How could he do it? "That's a bit more than a job a day," he said, swallowing hard.

"Your rewards in life will be based on the level of service you provide, multiplied by the number of people you serve," Cy said. "If you want to make a lot, you have to serve a lot."

Troy looked scared. "How am I going to sell a job a day? And then install an $18,000 job a day?" He searched for an answer.

Cy replied, "First of all, you're not going to do it on your own. Right?"

Troy took a breath. "Right" he said, not sounding comforted.

"Troy, you're worried right now because of what you know about the past. What have you learned so far about that?" Cy asked, almost demanding.

Troy thought. "The past does not equal the future," he said, as he flipped a few pages back in his book. He read the notes. "And the past has nothing to do with this conversation… and if I do what I've always done, I'll get the same results – but I am *not* going to do what I have before… and I should believe in myself. I mean I DO believe in myself." He finished and looked up.

Cy pointed the next question at Troy. "You told me there were other companies in your industry doing $30 million, or even $12 million right in your state, right?"

"Yes,"

"Well, are they better than you?" Cy asked.

Troy paused, getting his point. "No."

"There are no geniuses, Troy. They simply know something you don't know yet." Cy waited for it to sink in. Troy nodded.

Cy went on. "Now, in some businesses there is only a limited amount of work to go around. Like if you were a steeplejack, or say all you did was in-ground pools or home theaters. Then, in order to grow, you'd have to take work away from all the other guys; and still there may not be enough work for you to accomplish your goals. In your case, you've decided to specialize, but not so narrowly that the market is too limited for your goals." Troy listened.

"Who does all this exterior work that you want to get now?" Cy asked.

"Well, there are a few remodelers who are bigger, but it's mostly small guys – tons of them."

"Okay. Let me ask you — would these small guys subcontract from you?"

"A lot of them would work on my jobs, yes," Troy said.

"So then, the guy who controls the marketing and sales controls the business and can make a profit from those jobs, right?" Cy asked, like he knew the answer.

Troy slowly smiled. He knew that Cy had the answer. He wasn't completely sure what it was at this point, but he knew it must have to do with sales and marketing. Cy saw that Troy was satisfied enough for now that he could move on.

"So you need to sell 278 $18,000 jobs. Let me ask you — when you bid on a job, how often do you get it?" Cy asked.

"You mean my closing ratio? Well, for Piper it's around 12 percent most months, but for me it's around 45 percent," Troy told him.

"Oh. So what's an average, you think, for a decent salesperson who's not you?" Cy asked.

"About a third, I think," Troy said.

"Okay, so what's 278 divided by .33?" Cy asked, pointing to the phone on the table.

Troy punched in the numbers. "842," he said.

"Okay, so that's how many you need," Cy said.

"That's how many *what* I need?" Troy asked, perplexed. Cy just looked at him.

"Oh, oh, leads. That's how many leads I need," Troy announced.

Cy smiled. He knew he was taking Troy into new territory, and that Troy was doing his best to keep up. He could see that the young man was smart, and Cy had high hopes for him; but he also knew he was going to have to stretch him a lot more in other areas.

"How am I going to get 842 people to call me and say they want estimates?" Troy asked Cy.

"We're not worrying about 'how' at the moment, but do you know?" Cy asked, trusting that Troy already knew.

"Marketing?" Troy asked.

"You got it!" Cy told him. Troy thought for a minute and then shrugged, as if to say okay.

"So what're your business numbers going to look like?" Cy was asking Troy for a conclusion.

"Okay, I'm going to get 842 leads, sell 33 percent of them for $18,000 each — which would be $5 million in sales — have a 12 percent profit and make $600,000," Troy said, now sounding more confident.

"Very good, young man. I'm proud of you!" Cy told him.

Cy felt a sensation he was now familiar with. He knew that this lesson must end soon because he'd be gone. "Troy, write this down. I want you to work on this business model you've designed," he said, sounding as if he was in a rush.

"Okay," Troy said, sensing Cy's sudden urgency.

"I want you to measure how many leads you got last year, and from which towns. I want you to challenge the 842 lead number. How do you know you can get those leads, and from where? I don't want you to change the number; just write down all the challenges there are in getting that many. Then write down some possible solutions." Cy spoke faster.

"Do the same with the sales numbers – the 33 percent number and the $18,000 number. Write down challenges and think of possible solutions."

Troy wrote quickly. "You gotta' catch a bus?" he asked.

Cy continued, speaking fast and with purpose. "Write down the problems you can see with getting all the work done. Production problems and office problems, and some solutions. Then challenge the 12 percent number. How do you know you can make 12 percent profit? Write down problems with doing it consistently, and some ideas for solutions. Then write down why customers will think you are special. Why would they buy from you instead of someone else who has a lower price? Then figure out how many people you'll need in each department, and what that's going to look like. Get as close as you can figure, alright?"

"How am I gonna…" Troy began, but he was cut off as Cy continued.

"Call businesspeople at least two states away who are doing what you want to do, and ask them if they can talk to you for a few minutes. Keep trying until you get what you need to know." Cy sounded like he was finishing the dictation of Troy's homework assignment.

Troy spent 30 seconds looking down, writing fast. He heard a sound and looked towards it. It was a garbage truck emptying cans along the park road.

Troy looked back, and Cy had vanished.

Troy pulled out of the park, his mind stimulated yet exhausted; he was bewildered about Cy's disappearance. He looked for Cy for 10 minutes. He didn't want to leave him there in the park to walk home alone. But where was home? Troy still forgot to ask for Cy's cell number. And he didn't know anything about him. He knew by now that Cy was really here to help him… but why? Who had sent him? Who was he? Why did he come and go at the times and places he did?

Troy looked down at his cell phone. It said 6:15 p.m., 13 messages. Troy went home with a new sense of purpose, but it wasn't the same excitement that he felt yesterday. He was tired and there was work to be done – and he couldn't wait to get to it.

Chapter 9

Getting Started

"Yeah, Baby! Today is a good day!" Freddie declared as he strode through the office door.

Sandra looked up. "Well, I'm glad to hear that, Freddie. What's so good about it?"

"Well, first, here's a check from Kaspian," Freddie said as he playfully threw an envelope at her like a Frisbee.

"That's a good start!" Sandra said. "What else?"

"I gotta' tell Troy first. Where's he at?"

"He's in his office," Sandra told him. Freddie moved quickly down the hall.

Troy was toiling away at the questions Cy had assigned to him yesterday, ignoring the piles of work, messages and issues on his desk. Freddie came in excitedly through the open door.

"Troy. I got great news, man. You know the septic tank at Kaspians?"

"Yeah," Troy replied, like he couldn't wait to hear it.

"Well, it turns out they switched to city sewer 12 years ago, and that tank is abandoned!" Freddie said beaming.

Troy let out a huge sigh as he smiled. "Sweet!" he said.

"Yeah, so I'm just gonna' fill it and cap it and it will be all set today, and it's not going to cost anything, really," Freddie proudly informed him.

Troy sat back in his chair as it occurred to him how lucky he was to have a guy like Freddie running jobs for him. "Thanks, man," Troy said to him sincerely.

"Wait, that's not all. You know how the slider cost $1,100?" Freddie asked.

"Yeah?" Troy asked, now sitting up.

"Well, I was down at Hannans, you know. And I asked if I could look in that room under the trim shed — you know, where they have all the old windows and doors that they didn't sell, or were never picked up, or whatever." Freddie was excited.

"Yeah," Troy said, feeding off Freddie's juice.

"Well, I found that exact same door, in the back, all covered with dust, and it was damaged, but the door panel we need is perfect!" Freddie explained.

"No way!" Troy said.

"And I asked Skip how much, and he said it's probably been there for 10 years and … 50 bucks!"

Troy jumped up. "I love you, man!"

Troy and Freddie talked for a while about the jobs they had going. Troy told Freddie he was doing a great job and that he looked forward to a great future for him at the company. As Freddie went to leave the office, Troy yelled out to him, "They didn't have any stained glass windows in that room, did they?"

Freddie laughed as he let the door go. "We're lucky, but not that lucky!"

"Thanks, Fred!" Troy said, as he went back into his office, feeling good.

His joy faded as he saw the piles of work beckoning him. There were estimates to complete, mail to open, emails and voice mails to return. There were bills to approve, money to collect, and outstanding issues of many varieties. Troy stared at his desk, laden down with the urgent work of his business. He closed his blue book, noticing again the beautiful gold design on the cover, and set it aside. He dove into the piles, taking what was on top first.

At 6:45 p.m., he called home. "I'm sorry, honey. I lost track of time. I just have a few more things and then I'm leaving, okay?" He rushed, and more pieces of paper went from left to right, and the trash can filled up. He scribbled notes for Sandra and put his initials on bills that grew into a pile. He found a to-do list from several days ago, scanned it, and crossed off two items. At the top of the list he crossed off the word "Monday" and wrote in "Thursday." He stood up and looked at the larger picture of his office. He squashed cups down in the over-filled trash can, leaned all the blueprints in the corner, and put files and binders back in their respective crowded homes.

He grabbed his blue book and slid in into his soft briefcase, which he took with him everywhere. He straightened a picture on the wall and he went for the light switch, feeling some sense of accomplishment. He drove home, noticing the time on the dash — 8:37 p.m. Troy whispered to himself, "Damn."

The next day, Troy jumped into his normal routine. Coffee shop, office for an hour, run out to visit jobs, call subcontractors, check on the status of outstanding proposals, return calls from people who wanted estimates, more calls, more voice mail… Before he knew it, 6 p.m. came. He began wrapping up his day to go home. He wondered why he had not seen Cy that day. At 7:13 p.m., he hurried in the door to see what the family was doing.

Troy awoke early to the sound of heavy rain on the roof. He looked at the clock by the bed: only 5:12 a.m. He thought about the jobs he had going, and how the weather would affect his day. He got up about an hour earlier than usual, and had the idea of serving Karissa coffee in bed — something he hadn't done in a long, long time.

The coffee pot hissed and trickled softly as Troy sat at the kitchen counter. His bag sat right in front of him, and he slid the blue book out. After gazing at the cover, he opened it randomly. The page that opened before him contained two words. He didn't recognize the handwriting; it certainly wasn't his. It read: "Think Daily".

He stared at the words. "Who wrote this?" he said to himself. He flipped through the rest of the pages towards the back of the book, looking for other writing. Nothing. He flipped back towards the front, and there were all the notes he had written. The words "Think Daily" were written on the next blank page, after his own writing. Troy sat, thinking, looking at the words. He recalled that he hadn't done anything yesterday with the work that Cy had assigned him. He didn't look at his notes, didn't attempt to answer any of the questions Cy had asked him to work on, and didn't even look at the blue book.

"Where did Cy go?" he asked himself. Troy wondered if Cy would show up today. Then, a worry came over him. "I hope he doesn't show up today. He's going to be really disappointed in me," Troy whispered out loud in the quiet morning of the house. Then an idea struck him, and it grew in intensity over several moments, as he thought more about it.

"How can someone help me, if I don't help myself?" He looked down at the words. Troy had his motivation for the day.

Puffff. The coffee was ready. As the coffee mug tapped the nightstand, Karissa woke up. She looked at Troy and the coffee, and she smiled.

After making adjustments to the daily work assignments for the rain, which was beginning to let up, Troy sat down at his desk and pulled out the blue journal. He looked at his notes and tried to read what he had to do. He was hard pressed to find a spot big enough to open the journal all the way on his desk. There were still piles. He sat back and looked at the cluttered desk. His eyes went to this envelope, and that paper. He found himself thinking about the many things the papers represented. His eyes fell back on the blue book. "That's it!" Troy said, frustrated.

He stood up and walked out of the office. A minute later he came back with a folding table. He set it up near his desk. He took all the piles and papers from the desk and put them on the table, quickly trashing some papers from the bottom of the pile that were obviously very old. The desk was dirty underneath it all. He wiped the desk down, feeling great satisfaction over the simple task. He sat down and placed the blue book in the middle of the clean desk.

Before he opened the book, he paused. He looked to his left at the folding table with the piles. He thought for a long moment. Then Troy got up suddenly, grabbed the highest pile with two hands, and headed out for Sandra.

"Hi," he said, standing in front of her desk.

"Hi," Sandra said, sensing he had made some sort of resolution.

"Can you please go through this pile from my desk and take care of everything you can?"

Sandra raised an eyebrow and hesitated. "Really?" she said.

"Yes," he said.

"Well, what if things need your approval?" she asked slowly.

Troy thought for just a short moment. "You know what to do. If you don't know what to do, then ask," Troy said.

Feeling honored, she said, "I would love to go through that pile for you, Troy."

Troy took a breath and smiled at her. "Great."

As he walked back to his office, he saw Kara swoop in to help Sandra on the pile. He turned back. "Oh, and if anyone calls for me, can you see what it's about and try to take care of it?" Troy asked.

Sandra gave him another look of disbelief. "Absolutely," she said, feeling empowered, like she finally had been given something she'd always wanted.

As Troy sat down again at his clean desk, he glanced over at the folding table with the debris field on it. There was a 9-inch wide hole where the tallest pile once sat. "That was easy," Troy said to himself with great satisfaction. He turned to his blue book and opened it. For the rest of the day, he dug in to what Cy wanted him to consider, research and write. As he left the office at 5:54 p.m., it occurred to him – he hadn't gotten one phone call.

As he drove home, he felt a sense of satisfaction he had not felt in a long time. It was a great way to go into the weekend. He thought about taking Karissa and the kids out to dinner.

It had been three days since he had seen Cy. He wondered when Cy would be back. Or would he be?

On Monday morning, Troy went straight to Dingman's job to talk with Freddie and Mr. Dingman. When he returned to the office after that, Sandra was excited.

"Did you see what is left of your pile?" she asked, as she held up what looked to be just a few sheets of paper. She told him how she had chucked stuff that was old, already taken care of a half dozen things days or even weeks ago, knocked out a bunch of issues, and was looking for a few things that were in that pile. She explained that Kara helped her, and that they were a great team. "I just have four questions to kill the rest of the pile," Sandra said, eager to complete the task. He had no idea how she would complete it when he first gave it to her.

Troy stood there, embarrassed that he had been holding onto all that stuff. At the same time, he was relieved and overjoyed that they had helped him so much, and were happy to do it. It was as if he had made a new discovery.

"You guys are great!" Troy said, as he laughed with pleasure. He walked into his office, saw the table, stared at it a moment, and walked back out.

"Sandra, could you come here a minute?" Sandra walked into Troy's small office. "Grab the other end of this table, would you?" he said. They picked up the table and walked it to the side of Sandra's desk and put it down. "It's all yours," Troy said.

To Troy's surprise, rather than reacting with disappointment, Sandra looked over at Kara with a look that said Troy had just made both their lives easier. "Really?" Sandra said.

Troy said, "You guys are the best! Lunch is on me! You have no idea how much I appreciate it!" As he walked into his office, Troy thought about how he had gotten in the way of the normal flow of communication, transactions, and paperwork, by trying to do it all himself. Cy's voice echoed in his head. "Freedom comes when you realize you can't do it alone." Troy sat there, and said aloud to himself, "Nice job, bottleneck." He laughed out loud, and it felt good.

That day and the next, Troy worked on his "homework" as much as he could. He struggled with questions, spent time thinking about how he wanted his business to be, and outlined what problems he foresaw. He took each of Cy's questions as far as he thought he could.

"Troy, I want to show you something," Sandra said, as she opened a file drawer. "We organized all the stuff on this table into six folders. Whenever you need anything, they are right here. There are a few things you need to do, though. These people need estimates; these people are looking for their proposals; and there are four people you have to call because I couldn't help them, including the electrician for Dingman's. I really think we gotta' get a new guy."

Troy was witnessing a transformation. Not only did Sandra do what Troy had asked her to do, but she was taking on even more levels of responsibility as a result of him trusting in her. Sandra had worked at Troy Builders for three years as the office manager. But now he was impressed with her as never before.

Chapter 10
Lesson in the Library

Cy "awoke" to find himself at a quiet table. He looked around to find shelves with books all around him. "Where am I now?" he wondered. He thought about how Troy was doing, and how he enjoyed helping him, as dramatic as it was at times. Cy really felt he was making a difference, although he didn't know what any outcomes would be yet.

It was clear to Cy that he had been sent here to help Troy. He knew that if he could help him, it would affect the lives of all of Troy's employees, his family, his customers and his community – literally thousands of people over time.

"But why? Why didn't I 'finish my work' while I was here the first time? Why didn't I help anyone like Troy? Why didn't I reach out?"

Cy closed his eyes as images flashed before him. He heard a voice.

"Don't be cocky. Nobody likes a know-it-all." It was his mother's voice.

"Mom?" Cy called softly. But he knew it was just a memory. He recalled that, when he was young, he had been terrible at some things, but very good at many others. He focused on, and achieved in, the things he was good at. On occasion, he'd brag about how good he was, and he'd show off some. His mother, trying to build his character, cut him down when he'd needed it. It served him well overall, teaching him to be humble, and teaching him that he was no better than anyone else.

"I'm here to meet Donald Singer," Troy said.

"He'll be with you in a moment."

Troy was at Southern State University to look at some work the school needed done. He wasn't about to send Piper to estimate this job. Troy figured it could be a big, valuable job when Sandra first told him the university called for an estimate. Piper would probably blow it.

"Thanks, Mr. Singer. I know my company can handle this job for you perfectly. I'll get back to you with a written proposal by the end of the week," Troy said, as he left the facility manager's office. As Troy walked down the hall towards the exit, he passed a wall of windows. He stopped suddenly as he saw someone familiar. It was Cy, sitting at a table in the university library – with his eyes closed. Was he okay?

Troy walked around the corner to find a way into the library. He made his way back to a quiet corner where he saw Cy. It was him! He put his hand on Cy's shoulder. Cy was startled as he abruptly opened his eyes and looked to see who it was.

"Oh, Troy," Cy said, looking around bewildered for a moment. "Of course."

"What?" Troy asked.

"Uhh, nothing, nothing. I'm glad to see you," Cy said, shaking himself to attention.

"What are you doing here?" Troy asked.

"Ummm. Waiting for you, of course."

Troy looked confused and he hesitated. "Do you know Mr. Singer? I mean, is he one of your… ?" He stopped his question.

"Mr. Singer, never heard of him. Who's that?" Cy asked.

"The guy… uh, never mind." Both men decided to suspend their confusion in favor of what they were getting out of their meetings.

Troy stood there, holding his soft, worn leather briefcase, which he called his "bag."

"So, did you do your work?" Cy asked, motioning to the bag.

"Yeah," Troy said, hesitantly. "I'm not sure I got all the answers, and it took me a week."

"I knew it would," Cy answered. Troy thought for a moment.

"Wait a minute," Troy asked. "You didn't show up again until I finished the work you gave me? What if I didn't do the work?"

"Well then, you would probably not see me again," Cy said. "You know why, right?"

Troy thought and then asked, "Why?"

"Because if you aren't willing to help yourself, then there is nothing anyone can do for you," Cy counseled.

"Well, you don't have to worry about that with me, Cy. I'm a go-getter and I want this. I want it bad," Troy defended.

"I know," Cy said.

"So let's get started fine-tuning what your business will look like," Cy suggested.

"Okay, well the first thing I realized is that I am creating very specific business goals for myself to shoot for. Right?" Troy said.

"Very good," Cy said, obviously pleased with how Troy was starting. "Tell me your numbers goals again," he said.

"Okay. What I started out with was 842 leads or estimates given, times a closing ratio of 33 percent, which is 278 jobs sold; if the average sale is $18,000, which is $5 million in sales, and with a 12 percent profit margin, I would make $600,000 profit," Troy said.

"Okay, so did you challenge each number to make sure each was realistic?" Cy asked.

"Yes, Cy, and as I did, I realized how smart that is. I don't want to spend years chasing something that isn't realistic," Troy told him.

Cy raised an eyebrow as he nodded in approval.

Troy continued, "So, first I looked at how many leads I got last year. I was surprised to find that, between me and Piper, we gave 332 proposals, or an average of one a day. But when looking further, I saw we had another 94 leads that we just either didn't have time to estimate, or we went to look and just dropped the ball on them and never quoted. So that's 426 leads all-together, not even including the jobs that were not our kind of work. So on the lead side, we are halfway there," Troy explained.

"Okay, what else about the leads?" Cy asked.

"Well, if we are not going to do inside work, then about half those leads we got wouldn't be for us anymore. So really we only got 213 leads for exterior work, which means we are only 25 percent the way there," Troy said, now sounding disappointed. "But I'm clear that I hate inside work and want to focus on exteriors."

"So how do you know you can generate 842 leads?" Cy asked.

Troy went on. "Well, I have to say, we stink at marketing. I mean, we did some direct mail, which got okay results sometimes and poor results other times, and some yellow pages, which I don't hear people saying they got our name from very often. And we use yard signs sometimes and we letter our trucks. Word of mouth referrals were a good source because a lot of people know us, but there just aren't enough referrals for me to get 842 leads from," Troy explained.

"I'm glad you realized all this. But what's the solution?" Cy asked.

"Well, I have some ideas, but I'm not totally sure," Troy said.

"Let's hear them."

"Okay. Well, I know the Internet is important these days, and we don't do much on it. I mean, my niece made us a website, but nobody can find it unless they know our web address to start with. So we get next to nothing off of it. I think that's an area for big improvement," Troy said.

"Okay, good. Anything else?" Cy asked.

"Yes, one other thing. We only cover seven towns now, and the most we drive is 20 minutes in three directions, and 30 minutes to the north to catch more of the good neighborhoods up there. But if we add in a few more towns, we can get more leads," Troy said with satisfaction.

Cy cautioned, "Okay, great. Now I must say that when it comes to territory, you can spread yourself too thin. You have more people to market to, but your people and equipment are scattered all over the place. But you're only covering a small territory now, so I don't think you're in danger of that. Let me ask — how far can you drive each day to a job and still make it work for you?"

"I think we can drive 40 minutes."

"Okay, so why not draw a 40-minute ring around your location and cover that?" Cy suggested. "How many people would that be, compared to what you are covering now?"

Troy folded his arms, looked up and thought for a minute. "Maybe triple, or not quite. I can verify that when I get back to my computer. Oh wait, I can just look it up on my iPhone. It'll take a few minutes," he said.

"Well, don't worry about that now; you can verify the population later," Cy said. "Let's say it's two and a half times the population, to be safe. So you had 426 leads last year, and only half were for exterior work, which is 213. If we take 213 times 2.5 for the increase in population, that's what?"

Troy punched it in on his phone. "That's 532 leads," Troy said.

"Okay, divide that by the 842 you need, and that's what?" Cy asked.

"It's 63 percent of what I need, or 37 percent short," Troy answered.

"Well, do you think you can market in this larger area 37 percent more effectively than you are marketing now?" Cy asked, leading Troy that the answer was yes.

"Well, uh, there's one problem," Troy said. "I told you I started with these numbers. But I changed one, which changed a few others."

"Okay, I like this. What did you change?" Cy asked.

"Well, I originally said the average job was going to be $18,000. But after figuring and looking at the exterior jobs I did, and what I envision for the future, I had to change the number to $14,000. So that means I need more jobs to get to $5 million, which means I need more leads if the closing ratio stays at 33 percent," Troy divulged.

"Aha. Very good, Troy. You have been thinking!"

"I really have. I want this to work, Cy," Troy said. "I called other contractors, like you said. I researched the biggest ones at least two states away. You said that so they'd talk to me because I wasn't a competitor of theirs, right?"

"You got it," Cy said.

"Well, two guys were jerks and didn't want to help me. But then I found this one guy, Steve Addison, who runs a $10 million dollar company. They do interior and exterior and he was really cool and talked to me for an hour. He said I could call him anytime. Then I talked to another guy, Mike Haverson, who does $8 million, and he was very helpful too," Troy said, happy he followed through on Cy's instructions from their day in the park.

"Excellent. What else did you learn?" Cy asked, encouraging Troy.

"Well, I found out that Steve's closing ratio was higher than my target by a little, but he was really strong in sales management and his jobs were smaller than mine. And then another guy was a little under. So I'm going to keep my closing ratio target at 33 percent. But this means I need more than 842 leads with a $14,000 sale. I need 1,082 leads. So I need to expand my market area to a 40 minute radius, and be twice as effective at marketing to that population — which I can definitely do because, like I said, we stink at marketing," Troy said.

"Okay, so you decided what your business is – exteriors, and what area you'll cover – a 40 minute radius. And you know how many leads you need – 1082, and you have verified that the lead number and the closing ratio of 33 percent are realistic numbers to shoot for, as near as you can tell. And you know that your average job will be $14,000 and you'll have to install…" Cy looked to Troy for the next answer.

"357 jobs, which is $5 million."

"Most excellent, young man! Now, how about that profit margin number? How do you know that is accurate?"

"Well, I talked to the two other contractors and they are between 5 and 15 percent, depending on the year. They said an average is 11 percent for them, once they got established. So I'm going to make 12 percent happen," Troy declared.

"Okay, great," Cy said. "I like how you shot a little higher. It's not a good idea to use the average as a benchmark. But it's still realistic. I want to prepare you for one thing though."

"What's that?" Troy asked.

"Well, building a business takes capital. You will likely invest in trucks, equipment, materials, accounts receivable, and marketing. You'll invest this money out of cash flow, or a loan. If you are smart, you won't borrow money and you won't have to invest too much. But still, growth sucks up cash," Cy told him.

Troy looked puzzled. Cy continued, "For example, I see you have trucks. What does a truck cost?"

"$40,000, by the time we set it up and letter it," Troy answered.

"Okay, so how much business do you have to do to pay for the truck?" Cy asked.

"Forty thousand doll..." Troy stopped himself as Cy started laughing.

"C'mon. You are smarter than that!" Cy chided him.

"Oh yeah, well, uh, if my profit margin is 12 percent, then it's forty thousand times... I mean divided by point 12..." Troy tapped the numbers into his calculator. "Holy crap. Is that right?" Troy said as he punched the numbers in again. "I have to do $333,000 in business to make $40,000 to invest in a truck – is that right?"

"Sounds right to me," Cy said. "This is why so many contractors or small businesses make no money. Their yards and buildings are full of stuff they bought, representing the profits they would have earned otherwise."

Troy thought for a moment. "Well, I need trucks; we can't walk to work," he said, laughing.

"Yes, but can you buy a used truck for $20,000?" Cy asked.

"Absolutely," Troy responded.

"Well, how much business would you have to do to reinvest the profits to pay for a $20,000 truck?" the old man asked the young man.

"Obviously, half as much as a new truck, so that's $166,000. That's a lot better!" Troy said.

"Well, it's actually not quite as bad as that, because in your overhead before profit you will have some expense for trucks, but you get the idea. Spending half as much as you would otherwise means you have to only do half as much work to pay for it, and start making money for yourself again. You got that, right?" Cy asked.

"Totally. In fact, I wish I had bought a used truck instead of the one I bought brand new last year," Troy said.

"There you go," Cy said.

The old man fed out some ideas to Troy. "You could use subcontractors who have their own trucks, and require them to put your magnetic signs on their trucks when they work on your jobs. You could rent equipment that you don't use often. You must question every expense and question the big ones twice. Is there a way you can save money?"

"But I used to approve every bill, until a few days ago, and I couldn't keep up," Troy said.

"I'm not talking about micromanaging the bills all the time, although it is a good idea to do that once in a while. I'm talking about questioning what your businesses habits are, and what parts of your business model eat up your cash. It's different," Cy said.

"I see," Troy said, as he nodded rhythmically.

Cy went on. "In order to sell and install $5 million, you'll have to go on the offense in marketing and sales like you've never done before. And in order to make a 12 percent profit margin, you'll have to be defensive about spending the money you take in. The only way to make a 12 percent profit margin is to only spend 88 percent of the money you take in – right?"

Troy stopped moving and his eyes grew wide. "Right. It makes perfect sense. In fact, I could have been making 12 percent on the $1.5 million I sold last year — instead of nothing — if I was thinking straight and doing the right things!" Troy declared.

"Bingo!" Cy said.

"Crap. That's $180,000! What a dummy!" Troy said. Cy watched as Troy started grunting, like he was beating himself up.

"Listen, Troy. Your past mistakes are valuable. Had you not made those mistakes you wouldn't be prepared to understand what we talked about today in such a meaningful way. Mistakes and failure are part of the process of getting better. In fact, it's not possible to become successful without making mistakes. You just don't want to be making the same mistakes you made the year before," Cy told him.

"Well, I've been making mistakes for 12 years straight, and I'm glad I got them out of the way," Troy said.

"Well good, I like your attitude. Many people think they're failures because they make mistakes. You are not your failures, unless you make it that way," Cy told him.

Cy lowered his voice and looked straight into Troy's eyes. "Listen to me, young man. If you are to attempt something great, you will make mistakes. The question is — what will you learn from the mistakes - and how quickly?" Troy sat quiet on his words. He opened the blue journal and wrote it down.

"This is what I want you to do next," Cy said.

"Tell me," Troy said.

"Write down the answer to this question. Why would people buy from you instead of another contractor? Why would they buy from you even if the other guy's price was lower?" Cy said.

"Yeah, that's a big problem. Some guys bid so low, they don't even realize they're going to lose money, until they get the job almost done," Troy told him.

"Right," Cy said. "So how are you going to make homeowners buy at your fair prices, which are going to be higher than someone else's? What would they see is in it for them to do so? Put yourself in your customer's shoes. This is very important, Troy. Without this, your plan so far won't work."

"Okay," Troy said, writing.

"And don't say, 'They will buy from me because I'm charming' either, because you aren't going to be the one out there selling," Cy said. Troy looked up and they both laughed.

Cy continued his instructions. “Then write down how many people you’ll need in each department to make the numbers work.”

“Each department?” Troy asked.

“Yes, like marketing, sales, production, management, accounting,” Cy told him, talking faster.

Troy looked up. “Oh, oh, yeah, yeah.”

“Write, Troy. Write,” Cy said, sounding like he was in a hurry. “Write some ideas of who those people would be.”

Just then a woman approached the table. “The library is closing now,” she said.

Troy looked up and said, “Oh. Okay. Yeah, we’ll both be leaving then.” Troy saw the woman was confused. He looked across the table. Cy was gone.

She raised her eyebrows, her eyes scanning the room, and got a weird look on her face. “Oookay, then,” she said, as she walked away.

Troy drove home, vibrating. It was a good day. A very good day. He could see his future like never before – and he had created it. At the same time, he wondered how he was going to do it. But he decided to worry about that tomorrow.

Chapter 11

A Long Way To Go

It was a cool, clear morning as Troy stepped into the coffee shop. "Hey Chris! Hey Teddy!" Troy called out, happier than usual.

As Troy approached, Chris slid Troy's coffee across the blue Formica counter, worn so that the brown showed through in places. "How's that for service?" Chris said.

"You're the best!" Troy said.

"Usual?" Chris asked.

"Yep," Troy said, as he sat down at the counter by the window with Teddy.

"How's it going, my man?" Troy asked.

"Ahhhh," Teddy replied. It wasn't like Teddy to be down, so Troy knew something was wrong.

"What's the matter, Tedster?" Troy asked his friend.

"I bid seven jobs in the last two weeks and didn't get any of 'em," Teddy said, dejected.

"How come?" Troy asked, leaning in with great interest, remembering his latest homework Cy had given him.

"Well, I've been thinking about this, because I'm almost out of work, and this just isn't funny anymore. I mean I got kids to feed, ya' know?"

"I know, brother, so what happened with the jobs?" Troy wanted to know.

Teddy replied, "Well, two of them wanted these big jobs done but they couldn't afford it – or they didn't have the money, or whatever. And two were concerned about my reputation. I told them I had 18 years experience, but they just seemed like they weren't convinced. Man, I hate when you know you're a pro and the customer thinks you're a hacker," Teddy bemoaned.

"I know that feeling," Troy agreed, then added, "So what about the other three jobs?"

Teddy started unloading. "Well, that's what pisses me off the most. Three people in the last two weeks went ahead with another guy because his price was lower. And I know they don't know what they are doing – with estimating or the job — and they aren't gonna' do it right. I can't do a job for cost. I'm not gonna' do it. But what do you do when the people get a lower price, and they think they're getting a good job — but won't find out they aren't until after it's done? It sucks." Teddy took a sip of his coffee to calm down.

Troy sat with Teddy, and stared out the window, not saying anything. He felt Teddy's pain himself, and wanted to help his old friend. "All set, Troy," Chris said. Troy turned around to see his sliding sandwich come to a stop on the counter. He stood up and grabbed it and went back to Teddy.

"We're going to figure this out, Teddy, and I'm gonna' help you," Troy told him.

"What do you do?" Teddy commiserated.

"I don't know, but I'm going to figure it out. For both of us," Troy looked at Teddy, who was still gazing straight ahead out the window.

"Jackass patrol," Teddy said, motioning out the window. Troy could hear the obnoxious trucks before he looked up to see a parade of four black Spider's trucks take up all the spaces in the lot, as they parked sideways all over the place. "He doesn't have to worry. Every week the grass grows again and he doesn't have to sell the job again," Teddy complained.

"C'mon, you wouldn't trade places with lawn boy and you know it. I'll see you later," Troy said.

As Troy approached the door, the Spider's guys were coming in, led by their 6' 3" tattooed leader. "Hey, it's fair hair," Billy said, as he passed Troy. Troy let it go, like he had a hundred times before, knowing the day would come when he wouldn't. He just didn't have time to deal with Billy.

At end of the procession of black shirts, most of them with cut off sleeves, stood Danny, looking like he didn't belong. The look on his face told Troy the story. Danny didn't want to be there, but he needed a job and Troy didn't want him, either. He didn't look happy at all. "Hey, Danny," Troy said as he passed.

"Hi," Danny said quietly.

Troy greeted Sandra as he walked past her desk to his office. A minute later he came back to her desk. "I *thought* you had a smirk on your face. Thank you, thank you, thank you. It looks great!" Troy told her.

"You're not mad?" she asked.

"Why would I be mad?" he asked.

"Well, that we went in your office and didn't ask you?" she said.

"You guys did great!"

"It was Kara's idea," Sandra admitted.

"Well, when she gets in I'll tell her, too! Wow!"

Troy went back into his office that Sandra and Kara had cleaned and organized while he was out. They went through it all, and the room looked great. "Whew. Nice!" Troy said to himself. He sat down and pulled out the blue book.

Troy made time that afternoon to sit in his office and ponder some ideas about the big question that both Cy and Teddy had raised. He knew it was critical. On a yellow pad, at the top of a page he wrote, "How do I sell my services to homeowners when they can get a cheaper estimate?" He spent several hours thinking about things he had learned in the past, scratching notes and ideas. He got up and went into the main office room. He thanked Kara and chatted for a minute with his office staff, who was really giving things a great effort.

As he walked back into his office, he saw the blue book. The gold designs on the cover seemed to call him. He opened the book and looked at his latest homework notes. "Put yourself in the customer's shoes," he read. He sat back and thought.

Then Troy ripped off the page on the yellow pad that said, "How do I sell…" On a fresh page he wrote, "Why would a homeowner buy services from me when they have a cheaper estimate?" He became motivated just writing the question. He started by writing all the things he knew that concerned homeowners when shopping for remodeling. Then he thought about what he could do to satisfy their concerns before they made buying decisions. For several hours he thought and wrote. He was happy with himself for what he had done, yet he felt stuck, too, knowing it wasn't enough.

"Hello, this is Troy Becker. Is Steve Addison in?" Troy was calling his valued friend, and wondered why he hadn't called Steve hours earlier.

"Hi, Troy. We got your fruit basket. Everyone in the office thanks you very much."

"Well, I appreciate the help, Steve," Troy said. "Can I ask you another question?"

"Shoot," Steve said.

"Why do people buy from you instead of anyone else?" Troy asked.

"Ohhh. That's a big question," Steve told him. "That's THE question, and there are a lot of parts to the answer." Steve and Troy spent nearly an hour talking about it.

Troy called the other contractor, Mike Haverson. "Hi, Mike, this is Troy again. I have a question for you."

At the dinner table that night, Troy's mind was still engaged with all the ideas that came up in response to the question.

"What are you thinking about?" Karissa asked.

"There is just so much more I have to do with the business," he told her.

"More? How can you do more?" she asked, with a hint of sarcasm.

Troy thought for a moment. He knew she was worried that he'd never be home. "Right. No, no. Not more to do. Just different things to do. I have to make things work out better, so I can make money and be happy with it all."

She had to agree, and she nodded her head in a small motion. She didn't say anything.

Troy had not told her about Cy. He hadn't told anyone. He wasn't sure what to say about Cy, and he didn't have any answers if anyone asked the question, "Who was he?" Still, Troy wanted to tell someone about his new thoughts and goals.

"Have I told you my new income goal?" he asked Karissa, knowing he hadn't.

"No, what?" she said dryly.

"Well, if you're not interested…" he trailed off.

"No, I like income. What is it?" Karissa had lived through all the lean years with Troy, and watched him work harder and harder. She heard the triumphant stories about the new big job that was supposed to save them, only to hear about how the job went bad. Each night she followed the drama and the struggle. It wasn't as if Troy came home and downloaded all his problems every night; but when he did tell her about what was happening, she could read all the hopes and disappointments and frustrations and small triumphs that came with each story. Over the years they talked less and less about what was happening with the business, because it was just one year repeated, echoing the last.

Troy put it out there. "It's $600,000."

"Okay," she said, holding back a smile. "I have to take Hannah to Brownies," she told him as she got up from the table.

Troy knew she didn't believe him. Heck, it took some doing for Troy to believe it himself. It was a new idea, and he was determined to make it come true.

Karissa gathered up Hannah and made sure she had her things. Before she walked out the door, she came back to the table where Troy was still sitting with Tarin and Shelby. She leaned over and looked at him close. "Good luck," she said. Then she kissed him.

Troy was flying high the rest of the night.

"I got another one, Troy," Piper said as Troy walked into the office. Piper came around a lot when he sold something, and made himself scarce when he didn't, which was often.

"Great. Let's see. Tell me about this one," Troy said, as he motioned Piper into his office. When Piper left, Troy could see with new eyes that Piper had no idea what he was doing. But Troy believed that Tom Piper was a good guy, and doing his best at what he knew how to do.

Troy sat alone in his office and looked over the contract Piper had brought in. "Seems low to me," he said out loud, sounding disappointed, as he fingered his desk calculator. Just then, he heard the cushion on his guest chair squeeze down. He looked to his left and saw Cy.

A bit startled, Troy said, "You… holy…where do you come from?" Troy was still not so used to Cy coming and going the way he did.

"Hi," Cy said. "Did you figure it out?"

"I asked you first," Troy said.

"What?" Cy said, shrugging to tell Troy it was no big deal.

"Why are you here?" Troy asked again.

"I told you, and it hasn't changed. I'm here to help you. And right now, there is a big question that needs to be answered, isn't there?" Troy looked at Cy for a minute, and then let the question lead him.

"Why would people buy from *me*? Right?" Troy asked.

Cy got right into it. "Right. You can't reach your goals just because you want to. The only way you can get what you want is by giving enough people what they want. So what did you figure out?"

"Well, I made a list of things that people would be looking for when they call me or other contractors to look at their home, and then I made a list of things I could do to satisfy them, or be better than the other guy in that area. I hope I'm on the right track," Troy told his mentor.

"That is *exactly* the right track," Cy told him.

Troy was encouraged as he started. "Well, the number one thing people know about contractors is that we aren't very reliable. We could do bad work, not show up, not finish on time, take their money, you know – all that. So trust is a huge issue. I think it's the number one issue."

"I can see that in your business. As the price goes up, so does the customer's risk. It's different in every business. If you're selling something for two bucks, then trust isn't the main issue. Okay, good. So what are you going to do so that the customer trusts you more than anyone else?" Cy pushed.

"Well, that's the problem Cy. I think I'm… well, I don't know if I have too much about this. It's overwhelming. I talked to the other guys and got lots of insight, and wrote a million things down," Troy told him.

"Like what?" Cy said, understanding that Troy was overwhelmed. Troy looked at his list on how to build trust.

"Well, here goes. I have to have the right salespeople who look, act and talk like they are trustworthy, and who are good communicators and can listen. I have to ask more questions of the customers – that one's easy."

Cy interrupted Troy. "You mean *we*."

Troy got what he was saying quickly. "Yes. *We* have to ask more questions." He went on. "And we have to have a good marketing image – a logo, better paperwork, a better presentation, and we need testimonials – lots of them. We need case studies on the different types of jobs we did, with before and after photos to show new prospects. And we have to become experts at everything we do, and show that we specialize in what the homeowner wants. And we need to letter all of our vehicles better and wear uniforms, and get a great website, and show our licenses and insurance. And we have to try to get recognized and win awards or something to build credibility, and use video for testimonials, and show our work, and there's more and more…"

"Go on," Cy said, like he wasn't surprised.

"Well, we have to have a story about our company. We need to have some clearly communicated values that all our employees know and then communicate them to the customers – like integrity, and living up to our promises."

Troy took a breath and went on. "We need to be way better communicators, calling people more, and we need to give written estimates on the spot — or if we can't, within 24 hours. We need to get the jobs done right, and on time, too, if we're gonna' have people talking good about us. That's going to take some serious systems in production, because we're gonna' have a lot of jobs going on at once, and we have to keep quality up.

He continued, "We have to fix problems reported to us right away, and schedule right, and order materials on time so they are there when we need them, and hire the right subs, and communicate to them right, and make sure they are there when we need them, and have more systems in the office, and upgrade our phone system, and use email, and on and on and on…"

Troy rattled off. A sad look came to Troy's face. Cy watched him.

"It's gonna' take me 15 years to get all this in place. I'm going to be 50 years old by then," Troy said, looking prematurely defeated.

Cy looked at him. "Let's say it does. How old are you going to be in 15 years in any case?" Cy asked. Troy stared at him.

"The future is coming no matter what, young man. The question is, how's it going to be?" Cy said, as he slowly smiled.

Troy took a breath and let it out. "You're right," he said. "No matter how much work it's going to be, it sure beats the struggle I've had for the last 12 years."

They both looked satisfied that that was resolved. Cy looked down at Troy's long list. "Showing prospective customers you're trustworthy means first being the kind of organization that IS trustworthy. Doesn't it?"

"Yeah, and I've got a lot of work to do there. I mean, we're trustworthy, but customers don't see us like they need to, for us to be able to sell 357 jobs a year," Troy said. He corrected himself. "I mean for them to *buy* 357 jobs a year from us."

Cy smiled. "Remember this, Troy. All the resources, knowledge, people, experience, qualifications, values, systems, and skills of your company — and everyone in it — come to bear at the moment the customer is shopping for your service. When you can have a lot of great things to say, and show someone how you really can help them better than anyone else, then creating a sales system or process that works is a simple matter of communication and *how* you are going to communicate those things."

He continued, "If you don't have a company that really functions well, and that you and others are very proud of, then in order to win over customers you have to use smoke and mirrors. That's lying, and it never works for long."

Troy nodded. He was listening.

"Successful people think long term. People who only think short term aren't willing to make the investment, take the time, and do it right. And they wind up in trouble sooner or later," Cy added. Troy looked like he understood, but he was still deflated.

"It's a lot of work, huh?" Cy asked the young man.

"Yeah," Troy said slowly.

"Well, it's a lot of money, too," Cy added.

"What is?" Troy asked.

"$600,000," Cy reminded him.

Troy smiled. "Yeah, it is."

The wise man slowed his voice. "Troy, those not willing to change live a life like everyone else. Those willing to accept risk, step out of their comfort zones, and continually learn, live a life like no one else."

Troy soaked the statement in. He said, "If it was easy, I guess everyone would do it."

Cy smiled and nodded. "Here's the good news," he said, trying to perk Troy up. "You have a great start."

"I do?" Troy asked.

"Absolutely. You know what you want, and you're working on how to get there. Most people will never get even that far. And if you work on doing the *right* things every day, it won't take 15 years," Cy told him.

"How long will it take?" Troy asked, as if Cy had the answer.

"As long as you decide it's going to take," Cy told him.

Troy thought and asked, "What do you mean by that?"

Cy explained, "It depends on your attitude. If you think it's going to be hard and it will take a long time, then it will. If you think it's fun, and you work on building your business by doing the right things every day, and have a short time frame for its transformation into a $5 million dollar enterprise, then it won't take nearly as many years. It's your choice."

"Well, I choose fast!" Troy said.

"It's all up to you. It always has been," Cy said.

Troy stopped again to think on Cy's words, as he often had when talking to this man who has mysteriously and magically come into his life. Troy got lost in his thoughts, and Cy just sat there, letting Troy go.

Troy snapped to attention. "I can't wait to actually start working on the business," Troy said.

Cy again looked at him intently and lowered his voice. "Young man, you already have."

Chapter 12

A Clear Picture

Cy looked down at the cup of coffee that Troy never got to drink. "Oh, do you want a cup of coffee?" Troy asked.

"I'd love one," Cy said. "Black is great."

Troy walked out into the main office and his cell phone rang. "Honey, I'm going to take the kids to my mother's tonight, so if you want to work late, that's fine with me," Karissa told Troy.

"I tell you what. I'll work late and get some stuff done, and I'll come home tomorrow at 4 and we'll take the kids out somewhere," Troy suggested.

"Well, how about you take them out and I can go shopping in peace by myself?" she asked.

"That'd be great. Deal!" he said.

"Caffeine binge, or just thirsty?" Sandra asked, as Troy walked towards his office with a coffee cup in each hand.

Troy looked down at both cups and tried to think of what to say. "Ahhh, I'm just workin' on somethin' and, ahh, a little of both I guess," he said, walking away, without waiting for a response.

"Oh, that's good," Cy said, as he sipped. "Okay, now what's your business going to look like at $5 million?"

"What? Oh, ahh…" Troy flipped open his blue book. "I wrote it down and I even drew pictures." He tipped the book to show Cy stick figures and drawings of trucks and a building, and a few simple charts.

"I researched what the other guys had, and thought a lot about this.

First of all, I'm going to need someone working on marketing who specializes in it. Maybe not full time, but I need someone to get those 1,082 leads," Troy explained. "Then, I need seven salesmen. A good salesman can sell a million a year, or maybe more, but I need a few part timers to have some flexibility. My best full time guys will run a lead a day, but in this business it's a lot of work to do it right, so they'll need a break once in a while. So, seven salespeople."

"Then I'll need a sales manager to train, and make sure the salespeople are working effectively and customers are getting the service that'll be our new standard. And I'll need three more office people. One could be part-time, maybe. That's for accounting, and scheduling and phones and stuff," Troy said, like he was on top of it.

"Very good. I can see you're taking the visualization part seriously," Cy told him.

"Thanks," Troy said. "I'll also need to get 357 jobs done in a year, and if a job takes a week on average, I'll need seven crews of two to three men each. I'll have four crews working for me, and probably five or six crews I can sub to, so I have flexibility. Some guys specialize in stone walls and patios, some in driveways and landscaping, and of course all the carpenters in windows and siding and roofing," Troy explained.

"In addition, I need a really good production manager who has a couple helpers to manage all the work flow. That's a lot of communication and details. And we'll need systems to make it all work, and to keep everyone productive and the customers happy. I already have ideas on that. So with salespeople, that's at least 16 people in the office including me – sooo… we're going to need more space. I always wanted a really nice office with more windows and better parking, and some garage and shop and yard space. So that's what we're going to get," Troy summed up. "Is all that right?"

"I don't know," Cy said. "It's not a question of right or wrong. You can create whatever you want. It's your vision, so long as it works for your customers, employees and for you. That's the test. But it sounds great to me so far."

Troy looked relieved. "Oh, good. Well, I think this is it." He looked down at his paper.

"It may be, and it may not be," Cy said.

Troy looked puzzled. "What do you mean?"

"Well, it's great you've created a vision, financially and functionally. You're pretty clear on what it will be like, and you can step into that vision a whole lot faster that way. You can bring the future to life," Cy said. Troy nodded with satisfaction.

"But…" Cy said. Troy looked worried.

"But, it may not work out exactly this way. It may, and it may not. You'll find that out by trying. When you have problems, you'll need to make adjustments and even change your vision to make it work. You have to stay flexible. Planning is important, especially envisioning what you have so far. But you may find that things won't work out the way you thought, and you'll have to adjust as you go."

"If you aren't flexible, you could be stubbornly chasing some unworkable part of your original vision and waste a lot of years trying to do something in a way that won't work. Does that make sense?" Cy asked his student.

Troy bobbed his head. "Okay, I get that, yeah. Stay flexible."

"You can accomplish your financial goals lots of ways. Don't give up on your goal. With that, you are persistent. It's the HOW to accomplish it that you are flexible on," Cy added.

"Yes. I got it." Troy understood. He switched his attention back to his charts and notes. "What job am I going to do?" he asked, as he looked like he was deciding. "Cy, there's something I don't get."

"What's that?" Cy said.

Troy looked troubled. "Well, I mean if I was to do one of these jobs, uhh, well, there isn't any job that I'd pay someone $600,000 a year to do." Troy paused. They both waited for each other.

Finally, Cy said, "Young man, this is a shift in your thinking you must make. Did you ever have a job working for someone else?"

"Yes," Troy said.

"Well, that's called an employee. When you started your business you were working alone at first, right?" Cy asked.

"Yes," Troy answered.

"That's called 'self-employed.' At some point you hired people to work for you, right?"

"Yes," Troy followed.

"That's called being a 'manager,' and you are right. There are no manager's jobs in your plan that pay $600,000 a year." Troy looked at him, understanding what he was saying and hoping he had a solution.

"There's only one job that could pay $600,000 a year, if you were successful at it," Cy told him. Troy anticipated what his teacher would say next. "It's called leader. The business of building a $5 million a year company that spends only 88 percent of the money it takes in, pays $600,000 a year." Cy smiled easily at Troy.

Troy said to himself, "Wow." He was having a breakthrough. Cy let him sit with the thought for a minute.

Cy then asked, "How many dollars an hour is $600,000 a year?"

Troy turned to his calculator on his clean desk. "$240 an hour, if I worked 50 hours a week, and took two weeks of vacation."

"Okay, so in order to make $240 an hour, you must refuse to do any job that pays less than that," Cy told him.

Troy was still. Then he started to shift in his chair. "Now you really lost me. What could I possibly do that's worth $240 an hour?"

"I just told you, young man. Lead. Build the business. Put all the parts in place, like a machine, so that it produces the leads, sales, production, happy customers and profit that you need it to," Cy told him.

Cy continued, "Look, if you pick up a hammer and bang some nails for an hour or two because you're shorthanded, is that $240 an hour work?"

"No, I can pay someone $15 an hour to do that," Troy responded.

"What if you were searching and interviewing to get the best nail bangers, and enough of them, and training them to your systems. Is that $240 an hour work?" Cy asked him.

"Ohhhh. I see."

Cy looked at him. "Remember. The business is a reflection of you and your thinking and actions. You must be very clear on what your job is, and what it is not. When you're clear about what you must be looking at and doing each day, you'll get there a lot faster. So many business owners are caught up in the work, that they can't build the business that *does* the work," Cy said. Troy was soaking it up.

"Let me just tell you what your job will probably look like, in order for you to be successful," Cy began. "You are in charge of finding and hiring the right people and subcontractors. Do not take this casually. The wrong people will hold you back. We'll have to talk more about that later. You must build your business systems of marketing, communication, sales, management, accounting and production, so that your people are all doing it the same way. Building the system for others to do it, and *you* doing it, are two different things. You got that, right?" Cy asked Troy.

Troy was overwhelmed with the whole session with Cy, but at the same time he understood and was excited. He took a deep breath and sat up straight. "I understand that."

Cy went on. "You have to train and motivate your people, so they get the results you and your customers need. You have to nurture and reward your people, and hire managers who will do that, too. You have to position your company in the marketplace for success over your competitors, making adjustments of who your company is, to which customers."

"You have to measure results in each department, and always make adjustments to get better. And most of all, you have to be the kind of person that customers want to do business with, and your employees want to work for. That's what your job is," Cy finished.

Troy swallowed. "I see. And if I do it right, it's worth $600,000 a year?"

"Yes. And more. And if you screw it up, you wind up working all year for free. Or worse, you lose money," Cy said. The two men sat there for a long minute.

"Effective leadership is rare, Troy. But it's learnable," Cy told him. "You are no longer self-employed, and no longer a manager. You are the leader who is in the knowledge business, and information business, and decision making business, and most of all — the people business," Cy said. "You can do it, young man."

With that, Cy reached over and tapped on the blue journal, as if to encourage Troy to write it all down. "You best go home now," Cy told him, motioning to the clock that now said 8:30 pm. "Your family should be getting home soon."

Troy wanted to ask him how he knew that, but at this point, it didn't surprise him and it wasn't important. Obediently, Troy packed the blue book in his bag and stood up. He was inspired and in a state of higher awareness, as if he had been jerked from his old self that evening.

"Go on," Cy said, the old man still sitting in Troy's guest chair. Silent, Troy turned towards the door. He reached for the light, and turned back to look at Cy.

Cy was there, smiling easily, but looking tired. Troy left the light on and walked out to drive home.

Cy sat in the empty, silent office. He felt as if he had a gift to give, and he was making an impact on Troy's life. It was a rewarding and satisfying feeling, and one anyone would want more of. Then a sense of regret came over him. If he could have such an impact now, why didn't he help more people like Troy when he was alive?

Cy closed his eyes. A scene came back to him. He was on stage at school, receiving an award and a small scholarship for his academic achievement. He looked out into the audience for his parents. He finally found his mother's face in the crowd. He looked for his Dad, but only saw an empty seat alongside his mother. After the presentation, he walked off stage and worked through the crowd to find his mother. "Where's Dad?" he asked her.

"He had things to do, honey," she told him.

Cy and his mother pulled into the driveway. Light poured out of the open garage door into the night. Cy walked in through the garage and saw his Dad, working on the lawn mower. His Dad looked up. Cy held his certificate up so his Dad could see it.

"You gotta' take the garbage out; your brother did it last week."

Holding back the tears, Cy rushed to his room. The message was clear.

Chapter 13

Early Morning Lesson

Troy woke up early. He had trouble falling asleep because his mind wouldn't rest, and he was eager to take some action on his business. The more he learned from Cy and his two distant friends, and the more he thought about it, the more he wanted to get started.

He set off for the coffee shop in the still of the morning. The roads were quiet and he thought about what time Chris opened. The neon "OPEN" sign was on as he pulled into the nearly empty parking lot.

"What, did you get kicked out of the house, or what?" Chris said, looking at his watch.

"Nah, just getting an early start, changing it up a little," Troy said.

Chris nodded. "Here you go," he said as he slid the paper coffee cup across the counter. "It's gonna' be a minute, 'cause I gotta' warm the kitchen up. Manny's not in yet."

"No problem," Troy said.

As Troy made his way past the newspaper rack, which he ignored as usual, he looked around the corner into the dining room. "Wouldn't you know it?" Troy said to himself. He made his way to the back corner where he saw Cy sitting.

"Morning," Cy said.

Troy smiled and sat down. "Good morning," Troy said. "I gotta tell you, Cy, I'm excited. I am ready to go. And it won't take long."

"You're going to need enthusiasm, that's for sure," Cy said.

"Well, I've got it. I thought about some people I can hire that would be perfect for the job, and I'm gonna' look at a new building today, and I'm gonna' make my business look like my drawing very quickly."

Cy smiled uneasily. "What?" Troy said, sensing Cy was worried about what Troy told him.

"I don't want to discourage you or anything… but," Cy said.

"But what?"

"Troy, it's easy to spend money, and hard to make it," Cy told him.

"I know that," Troy said, having no choice but to agree.

Cy continued, "Many business owners get excited about spending the money to make their company LOOK like it's successful, before it actually is. That may be wise and necessary in some businesses, but not in yours."

Troy had come to trust in what Cy was saying, and although the wind had just been sucked from his sails, he had to know where Cy was going with this.

"When the expenses get ahead of the income, you have a problem – and it could kill you. Do you have any money to pay new employees or buy a new building right now?" Cy asked.

Troy slumped his shoulders. "No," he admitted.

"So spending new money is not possible right now then, right?" Cy told him.

"Right. But then how…" Troy asked frustrated.

"Don't worry, Troy. You're going to do all those things. It's just a matter of IN WHAT ORDER you do them," Cy told him. Troy saw a hint of relief from his dilemma now.

"You have to create some value first," Cy counseled. "Then you can use it to invest in your growth."

"What do you mean, create some value?" Troy asked.

"Fix what you have," Cy said.

"Fix what I have?"

Both men heard a voice over the intercom system in the small shop. "Troy, your sandwich is ready, buddy." Troy got up, walked around the corner to the counter, and saw his breakfast wrapped in wax paper sitting on the counter. Chris had already gone back in the kitchen, preparing for the day.

"I know what you're talking about," Troy said, as he went back to the table. "You're talking about, I need to work on the business I have, so I can make 12 percent on the $1.5 million business I already do. Right?" he asked Cy.

"Right. You don't want to expand a broken business, do you?"

Troy got it now. "Ohhhhh. I get it. You're absolutely right," Troy said, some of his enthusiasm coming back. "So what do I do first?"

"There's lots you can do to get better results without making any significant investments of money, so you can start doing better. Make a system for production that is scalable, for example," Cy suggested.

"Scalable?"

"Yes. Any system you put in place, any process for your employees to follow, must work — even when you have two or three or four times as many employees or crews or salespeople employed. You don't want a system that only works when you are small. Then you have to reinvent it when you grow and do that work all over again," Cy instructed.

Troy nodded and reached for his blue journal. Cy continued, "As the owner, this is valuable work. It's a high value activity — the kind of thing you should be working on. And the highest value activity is what I used to call a 'Legacy Project.' That's a project you work on that, when complete, lives on for years and years, producing results far into the future," Cy explained.

"Okaaay," Troy said slowly, as he wrote in the blue journal.

Cy noticed with satisfaction that the cover of the book was still new looking, even though many pages were filled with notes. He said, "When you work on a part of your business, no matter how long it takes, do it really well. Make that part, that system, really great so you don't have to work on it again. No matter how long it may take. You can always go back and tweak it, and you may have to. But don't be like most business owners. When they have a big problem in one part of their business, they tinker with it for a few hours and call it done. They never really overhaul the process so it gets fixed right, and they continue to have the problem forever."

Troy looked up partially from the journal and stared at a spot on the table for a long moment. "Yes, it is a lot of work," Cy said.

"How did you know what I was thinking?" Troy said.

"I could hear it on your face," Cy told him.

"How am I going to overhaul all these functions, all these parts, all these employees, all these systems? I mean, I have no time, and how do I know what to do anyway?" Troy moved from excitement back to overwhelm, as he often found himself doing since he met Cy.

"Troy, Troy, Troy. First of all, you don't overhaul people. You train them, tell them what you expect, set up an environment for them to succeed, and give them your support and understanding. But let's talk about that later." Cy continued. "Finish my sentences – The journey of a thousand miles begins with..."

"A single step," Troy said.

"You don't have to be great to get started, but you have to get started to be…"

"Great?" Troy added.

"Yes. How do you eat an elephant?" Cy asked, smiling now.

"One bite at a time,"

"See? You know this stuff. Whether you get overwhelmed or not depends on your attitude," Cy told him. Troy started nodding.

"I know it sounds like a lot. But remember this. Business is a competition. Other guys want the same business that you want. But it takes mastery of seven different elements to make the business really competitive — to really win big," Cy explained.

Troy had his pen to the paper. "What are the seven areas?" he asked.

"You," Cy started.

"Me?" Troy interrupted.

"Yeah, you. The leader's mastery of him or herself."

"Oh yes. We've been talking about that for a while now, right?" Troy asked.

"Right. So first You, then Leadership, Team, Marketing, Sales, Production or Operations, and the Numbers. Those are the seven areas. And within those seven areas there are many pieces of knowledge," Cy explained as Troy wrote.

"I know it sounds like a lot. But you want to win, right?" Cy asked him.

"Yes," Troy said. He sat up straight.

"You want to make your goal, right?"

"Yes," Troy said firmly.

"Look, the business owner who can master more of these areas than his competitor will win out. The person who can assemble and integrate the greatest number of these skills into his business will have the advantage in the marketplace. For example, if one business is good at marketing, it'll get lots of leads. But if a competitor is not only good at marketing, but good at sales as well, that business will have an advantage. If a third business is good at marketing, sales, and building the best team, then they will have the advantage," Cy told him.

"I'm following you," Troy said.

Cy continued. "This is why you can work on your business for a long time, and make progress in it, but not get the sales and profit results right away. It may not be until you have the synergy of excellence in two, then three, then four and more of these seven areas that you begin to see the results at the bottom line. But as long as you are achieving excellence in another one of these seven areas, you are getting better, even if it doesn't show up on the bottom line — YET."

Troy understood what his mentor was saying to him. As Cy sipped his coffee, Troy thought for a moment. "Is it true that if a business is weak in one area, that will hold it back?" Troy asked.

"No doubt about it, Troy. You're a smart kid. Yes. The area that a business is weakest in will set the height of its success. For example, if your business was terrible at production, then that's going to hold you down, right?" Cy asked.

"For sure," Troy said.

"If you were really bad at marketing, then that would hold you down, right?" Cy asked.

"Right."

"And if you were really bad at *sales*..." Cy said, like he knew something Troy didn't know he knew.

Cy sipped his coffee. Troy unwrapped his sandwich, which was now cold, and took a bite. As he chewed, he sat back with his arms folded; his wheels were turning.

"Well, how do I know how to do all this stuff? I mean, how do I know about the seven areas myself?" Troy asked.

Cy smiled and paused before answering him. He spoke slowly. "That's why you have to work harder on yourself than you do on your business. Everything you need is already all around you. You just have to tune in; and when you do, you will see things you never did before, and things will appear in your life when you need them," Cy told him.

"You got that right," Troy said.

Cy continued. "Become a learning machine. Because in the end, you create value not by doing, but by knowing *what* to do. You are your value. It's what you become — in the process of building your business — that is your true wealth. If something happened and you lost everything tomorrow, you still know how to build a business, and you're still wealthy."

Troy sat in Cy's words for a long while.

Cy asked, "So, do you know where to start now?"

"I think so," Troy replied.

Cy softly challenged Troy. "Time to get started."

"Hey, Troy. What are you doin' back here by yourself?" Troy snapped his consciousness back into the room and looked up to see Teddy standing by his table.

"Oh, hey Teddy." Quickly, Troy looked back at Cy. But just like that, Cy was gone.

"I'm gonna' go order. You want another coffee?" Teddy asked his friend.

"Naw, I'm good, man. Thanks," Troy replied. He sat there alone, feeling alone, yet as sharp and focused as he had ever been in his life. He gathered his book, his bag, and what was left of his cold sandwich, and made for the door. "Gotta go," he called out to Teddy, without waiting for a response.

He started his truck and pulled out of the lot. A voice came over his truck speakers. He didn't recognize the program. Troy turned the radio tuner dial, but it wasn't the radio. Confused, he pressed Eject. A CD popped out of the player. Troy read the label. "Reimagine."

"What the?" Troy said out loud. On the seat next to him was the rest of the program.

He pushed the CD back in.

Chapter 14

Rallying the Team

"Good morning," Troy said to Sandra as he walked into the office with Freddie. "Can I talk to you and Kara for a few minutes?" The four of them sat down at a table. Sandra and Freddie wondered what was up, because Troy was acting differently than he ever had. He didn't normally have meetings like this.

"I would like to announce that we are making changes," Troy told the three of them.

"Uh-oh," Sandra thought. Freddie sat there wondering if it was good or bad. Kara didn't know what to think, since she hadn't been there that long.

Troy went on. "We have a pretty good business here, but compared to what we can do, we're struggling. And the first thing that I want to tell you is that I take responsibility for it all. You guys are doing a great job. And I want to thank you for that. I want to change this business for the better for all of us, and as far as changes go, I'm going to start with me. I have been working hard, but not on the *right* things. I want to grow this business, and in order to do that we are going to need better systems and procedures for marketing, sales, scheduling, production management, ordering, and accounting," a new Troy told his team.

The three listened, not knowing what to make of their boss. They had never heard him talk like that, and they didn't know what to say at the moment. Troy continued, "We need to have procedures, so that when we have more business, and do more jobs, we don't have more problems."

Sandra and Freddie nodded in agreement, beginning to get in on the conversation. Troy looked at each of them and said, "I need your help. I can't do it without you. I know you're working hard now, and I am not asking you to work harder. But I am going to ask you for your talent in other ways. I need your ideas on building the business procedures we need. If you have an idea on *ANYTHING*, I want you to share it. And when we do this, and build a great business we can all be proud of — one that is a leader in the community — we will all be rewarded. A rising tide raises all ships," Troy told them, and then he waited to see how it was landing on them.

Freddie smiled and nodded his head, then finally spoke. "I'm with you, Troy. It sounds great. What exactly did you have in mind?"

"We are going to do 357 jobs in a year, at an average of $14,000 a job. And we'll be a $5 million company, instead of a $1.5 million company, like we are now," Troy said, sounding very confident. The team seemed amazed at Troy's precision.

"Did you go to a seminar or something?" Sandra asked playfully. They all laughed for a couple seconds.

"Kind of," Troy said. He continued, "The fact is that I've always wanted to have a winning company, and to strive for excellence. You guys know that." The three of them nodded in agreement. "I just needed to learn some things and get a more clear vision of exactly what I wanted."

"Yeah, 357 jobs is pretty exact," Sandra said. Again they all laughed.

"I know. And I know we've had our troubles, and there will be challenges in the future. But we can do it, and we will," Troy summed up. They sat there, looking at their leader, half excited and half wondering if his declaration was real, or if it would last.

"I'm in, brother!" Freddie said. "I've worked at a bunch of different places in the past, and nobody ever wanted to do something great. But I wanted to find somewhere that would try – and I'm glad it's here," Freddie added. Troy smiled.

Sandra spoke up. “Troy, you know I am behind you, whatever you want to do.”

Troy softened his voice to respond to Sandra, who was always trying to take care of him. “I know. I appreciate that.”

Then Kara spoke. “Troy, I’m graduating soon, and I have a lot of ideas. I’ve been researching and studying how other companies deal with stuff, and I know I can help out.”

“Great, Kara. Well, this is a place where your ideas will be valued and considered. I want to hear it all,” Troy said. The three employees sat there beaming. Troy could see their wheels turning already.

“When do we get started?” Freddie asked.

“Right now,” Troy said. Sandra stood up to get yellow pads and pens for everyone.

Troy pulled the flip chart near the table and got up. “This is the plan,” he said. He told them about his vision as exactly as he had figured it. He told them about how many leads they needed, about how many salespeople they needed, and about how many crews they needed. They discussed it back and forth. A few skeptical questions came out, but Troy either gave them answers, or encouraged them by saying they’d figure it out together.

“So, what do we do first?” Freddie asked.

“First we have to fix the business we have, so we can grow it,” Troy said. Kara and Freddie nodded vigorously, while Sandra looked puzzled.

“I mean, we need to get the right systems and people in place for selling, for scheduling, for production, for the subs, and for accounting. I mean, if we can’t handle this volume, then we can’t grow, right?”

"I hear that," Freddie said.

Troy added, "If we're going to sell more, we have to have a structure and get good at it – really good. And if we're going to schedule and do work and hire subcontractors, we need to get good at that – really good." They all agreed. Sandra looked like she had something to say about that.

"So the first thing I want you to do, Sandra, is think about how we can handle the sales leads better, and create a system for scheduling salespeople that will work when we have seven of them – heck, 14 even," Troy said.

"Well, Kara does that with me, so we'll work on it together," Sandra said.

"Perfect," said Troy. "And Freddie, we need a production management system. You and Sandra can think about that. We're going to have seven crews, and many subs, so we need to have a super-organized system."

"I think we can do that," Freddie said.

"What about marketing? I mean, where are all these 1,082 leads going to come from?" Kara asked.

"Oh, yeah. We're going to hire a marketing person," Troy told them.

Sandra perked up. "That'll be great, because I won't have to do it. If I'm going to do more of other stuff, it will free me up to focus on production management and accounting. There's going to be a lot more of it," she told the three of them.

Troy wrote the numbers clean and neat on a full flipchart page, and tore it off. Kara taped it to the wall. "I don't think Piper is going to like this," Sandra said.

Troy looked at her and said, "I know. He's probably not going to like it one bit."

The small team broke up to go back to their duties. Troy was relieved that they not only took it well, but were eager to contribute and build the business into something better. In fact, they almost seemed relieved that it was happening, like it's what they had wanted all along.

Piper walked into Troy's office with little enthusiasm. "You wanted to see me?"

"Yeah, sit down. Piper, you've been here a long time, and I think we know each other pretty well," Troy began.

"Yeah..." Piper let out with anticipation.

"And you know I like you. But it's just not working out," Troy said, bravely.

"You can just say it, Troy. I've been fired five times in my life, and I know what it sounds like," Piper said, trying to cut his agony short.

"I want to thank you for working here, and for all your efforts over the years, and I wish you luck. Really," Troy finished.

Piper got up. "Thanks," he said coldly, and walked out.

"You did the right thing, Troy," Sandra said to Troy as he walked out into the main office after Piper left. "He was no good. Nice guy, but he was hurting us. You know that." Sandra knew that Troy cared for his employees, and knew he liked Piper, and it was hard for Troy to fire him. "In fact, Troy, in order for us to reach our goals, we had to let him go," she told him.

"I know," Troy said. "It still stinks."

"Hey, guys. I got the weirdest phone call. You're not going to believe it," Kara said from her desk across the room.

"What?" both Troy and Sandra said in unison.

"This guy called. He wouldn't say his name. He told me that Troy should know that Piper has been selling jobs for Spiders Remodeling," Kara said.

"Spiders?" Troy perked.

"Yeah. He said that Spiders is starting to do remodeling, and that Piper has been bringing him sold jobs for at least two months. He said that Spiders paid him two percent more commission than Piper got here. He gave me an address of one job – 27 Corning Ave.," Kara said, looking at her notes.

Sandra saw that Troy was upset. "When did he call?" Troy asked.

"I just got off the phone with him," Kara said.

"Well, what else did he say?"

"That's it. He said that's all he knew, and he just said to tell Troy," Kara said.

Sandra was sitting at her computer, looking at the screen. "That was our lead! I sent Piper out on it six weeks ago and he said that they changed their mind and didn't want an estimate."

"That son of a... " Troy began to erupt, and then stopped himself and took a breath.

"I guess I already solved that problem, didn't I?" Troy said.

"Good instincts!" Sandra congratulated him, both of them trying to reframe the situation.

"Spiders," Troy grumbled in a whisper, shaking his head.

"Oh, one more thing," Kara said. "The caller… I could be mistaken but… it sounded like Danny."

The next morning, Troy pulled up to the coffee shop to see Spiders trucks already in the lot. He steeled himself. He didn't want to go to another coffee shop to get away from the "pirates" — after all, he had been going there for years; it was his place with his friends. But Troy knew that all the Spider guys were laughing at him, knowing their boss was getting over on him.

As Troy walked through the lot towards the door, he noticed one of the trucks had a magnetic sign over the Spiders Landscaping sign that read, "Spiders Remodeling; Additions, Decks, and Renovation."

"Bastards," Troy said to himself.

When he walked in, he saw Billy at a booth with his posse. "I should just kick his ass right now," Troy said to himself. But his cooler head sent him towards the counter.

"What's a matter?" Chris said to Troy.

"Is it that obvious?" Troy asked his friend.

"Yeah," Chris told him.

"Friggin' guys," Troy said, motioning to the band of tough guys.

Chris lowered his voice. "Don't worry about them, Troy. I hear stuff all day. Billy's got his coming. You don't have to do a thing." The wise shop owner continued, "And you know, most of those guys are okay. It's just Billy, you know. I don't know why he does what he does. He's okay, deep down; I just don't know why he acts like a jerk. It makes him look tough. That's all. But he's not," Chris said, putting some perspective on the situation.

This was one of those moments when Troy valued his friendship with Chris the most. Chris always had a good angle on things. Troy took his coffee and turned to sit at the counter, refusing to just get his breakfast and run.

Then it dawned on Troy. Billy hadn't been his usual jerk self to Troy this morning. In fact, he hadn't said anything, but was sitting quietly instead. It was as if Billy knew he had stirred Troy's pot, and didn't want to press his luck.

Just when Troy felt he could think of nothing else, he heard a voice in his head. It was a recollection of Cy telling him to work on high value activities. He decided that Spiders was not one of them. There was plenty of work out there, and one more remodeler wouldn't make any difference at all. Besides, it occurred to Troy that building his business to match his vision would be the greatest statement of all.

That day, Troy got into his mission, which he held in his head most of the time. He now went through his daily duties of sales, checking jobs, scheduling, and dealing with subs, through new eyes — the eyes that wanted to build a system to make these tasks automatic and simple and structured, so anyone could do them. For the moment, he forgot all about Spiders.

"Hello. Mike Haverson in?" Troy was calling one of his long distance counterparts and advisors. "Mike, I have a few more questions for you. Is this a good time?" When he hung up he called Steve Addison to ask the same questions, and a few more.

Sandra came into Troy's office and slipped a note under Troy's nose. "Your first candidate is here for the interview."

Troy interviewed many candidates for the sales job, as his advisors counseled him. Out of 14, he picked two. He had his eye on another, but he just didn't need three right now.

The first was an older man named Harmon Greentree. He was an industry veteran who had been selling home improvements for 25 years. Not only did he know how to sell very well, but his community involvement was impressive. The last company he worked for had folded, through no fault of Harmon's, because the owner retired and had nobody to take over, and he couldn't sell the business.

The important thing about Harmon was that he was also a strong sales manager. He could start as a salesperson, and move up into the management spot when necessary. Troy really liked this guy's attitude and the experience he brought to the company.

The second guy was a 37-year-old salesperson named Max Brady, who had been selling for his whole career — the last nine years of it in home improvement. He seemed to be an expert salesperson, having been trained at another company that was very disciplined about sales training. He also had a great attitude, and was looking to plant himself at a company that was growing and had good management.

Troy had talked to both candidates four times in person, and had at least one lunch with each of them, before making his decision. Another finalist was rude to the waitress at lunch, so he was disqualified.

"Wow, you are serious!" Sandra said. Troy had introduced his two new salespeople to Sandra that afternoon, and they went home to prepare for the leads Sandra said she had for them the next day. "Now, with two full time guys we'll never be struggling to tell homeowners when we can get there to give them an estimate! That makes things a lot easier!" she said, happy that she finally got something she always wanted.

"Yes, and if they can sell, I won't have to. And that frees half my time up to work on the rest," Troy told her with much hope and enthusiasm. "Listen, though. I need time to train them. So let's not book them up too much, just yet."

"Well, I can't overload them because I don't have that many leads right now," Sandra told him.

"You know, they were both a little disappointed we didn't have very good sales tools, but Harmon in particular said he could help us with that," Troy said, as he made preparations with Sandra to set the guys up for the next day.

As Troy drove home, he was excited. "Where have these guys been all my life?" he wondered.

"I haven't been in the office all day – ever!" Freddie told Troy.

"Well, now we're getting things done!" Troy kidded him. They had scheduled a two-hour meeting in the morning to work on their production management system, to make things run smoother now; and after, they scaled up. The meeting turned into all day, but nobody cared because they were very proud of what they had designed. Throughout the day, Sandra and Kara were listening and adding ideas, and it turned into a four-way brain trust.

"I almost forgot," Freddie said, producing an envelope. "Here is the FINAL check from Mrs. Kaspian!" He said it triumphantly, slapping it down on Sandra's desk like a wide receiver who had just scored a touchdown.

"Congratulations, Fred! Great job!" Troy said.

"And she said that, despite what happened, she liked how we handled everything in the end, and she was very happy and would be glad to refer us!" Freddie declared. "Okay, so what we have to do is go over there and take a testimonial video, the 'after' photos to go with the 'before' ones, and bring her a small gift, and ask for referrals. I'll do that myself," Troy said.

"Video?" Sandra said. "What are you gonna' use that for?"

"I don't know, but I have a feeling video will be very useful in our future, and I want to get there and video her while she's happy with her new project."

Just then, Harmon walked into the office. "Got one!" he exclaimed with excitement.

"What? Already?" Troy shouted.

"Yep, my first lead. And you're going to love these people. They're dream customers! I got them approved through that finance company I was telling you about that I've been using for the last year," Harmon told the whole group.

"What was that job, and how much?" Troy asked.

"It's a new roof, a tear off, which was what they called about, and I saw that they needed a driveway, so I sold that. And we're replacing a block retaining wall with a stone one," Harmon informed them.

"That's a nice job!" Troy interrupted.

"And…" Harmon continued, "we're rebuilding their back porch – it's just very small, but that's included, too. But it's a big driveway and the retaining wall is 56 feet long."
"Sweet! Just what we want – all exterior work!" Troy encouraged. "How much is it?"

"$27,540!" Harmon declared.

"I think you're going to work out just fine," Troy said, and everyone laughed.

"Congratulations!" Freddie told Harmon. "I like you already!" he said in his positive, likeable way.

Troy went home and told Karissa about his day, and showed his excitement for what was happening. He told her about the new production system, and the ideas he had for even better things. Most of all, he couldn't believe his new salesman had sold his first appointment – and such a large job!

"It was his first appointment!" Troy told her, shaking his head.

"I never liked Piper that much anyway. He seemed sneaky to me," she said.

"I think this is really, finally, going to work out," Troy said with satisfaction. Karissa had to admit to herself that things were happening, and happening faster than she had ever seen before.

As they shut the bedroom light off that night, they both lay there, looking up. "I'm proud of you," she said softly. He reached over and grabbed her hand, and held it until they fell asleep.

Chapter 15

Disaster

As Troy walked into the coffee shop, he looked to the back corner where he had met with Cy days earlier. He hadn't seen Cy in a while, and wondered if he'd ever see him again. He panicked for a moment when it occurred to him that he hadn't thanked Cy.

While there was much more to do, and he hadn't made any measurable progress towards his financial goals, he could see the wheels of positive change in motion. He felt like he had in the years when he first started his business, when everything was new and fun. He was alive and he didn't feel stuck. It wasn't that he knew everything he had to do yet, but he felt he could find the solutions as he needed them. He was confident in himself.

Troy thought about the way Cy had come and gone. Cy disappeared before Troy could ever thank him, and he didn't know how to call him.

Teddy and Phil, Troy's contractor friends, were both seated at the window as Troy walked in. "Hey, Troy," they said together.

Troy grabbed the coffee that Chris had already put on the counter and turned to sit with his friends. "Hey, guys," Troy said.

"What's new?" Phil asked.

"A lot," Troy said convincingly.

"Whoa," Teddy said. "Listen to Mr. Enthusiasm!"

"Hey, what can I say? It's going good," Troy insisted.

"What are you doing? Because I could use some of whatever it is," Phil said, interested.

“Me, too,” Teddy agreed.

“Well, I learned that you can’t get better just standing there. If you want a good business, you have to study business, and learn, and improve your knowledge and earning ability.”

Troy spoke to his two self-employed friends to help them. He wanted to share what he knew – or at least what he had learned so far. He knew he had a long way to go, but he felt he could offer them something.

“Did you go to a seminar or something?” Teddy asked.

“You might say that,” Troy admitted. “I’m making changes to go big. I want a big business I can be proud of, that doesn’t cause me ‘agita’,” he said.

“So tell me one thing,” Phil challenged.

“Well, if you have a bad employee you’ve been putting up with, who you are afraid to fire — fire him,” Troy said.

“Who’d you fire?” Teddy asked, knowing most of Troy’s employees.

“Piper,” Troy told him.

“I knew it,” Teddy said.

“Well, that’s kind of obvious. That’s it?” Phil asked.

“No, no, no,” Troy said. “Umm… you have to have a very clear picture of what your business would look like if it were perfect – you know, what your vision is, exactly,” Troy told them.

“Well, my vision is to make a lot of money!” Phil said.

"Well, see that's what anyone would want, but that's not a clear enough vision. The profit is a byproduct of your business. So unless you get the business right, you won't have any money," Troy counseled.

"I'm an expert on not having any money!" Teddy said. They all laughed.

"Yeah, you still owe me $20, you deadbeat!" Phil said to Teddy.

"I'll get it to you when my wife gives me my allowance, which is if I ever get paid from this big tile job I finished last week," Teddy told them.

"No seriously, Troy. I need to do something different, 'cause this is gettin' old. I've been a carpenter for 14 years, and I love the work, but the business is killing me. Can you help me?" Phil asked sincerely.

"Me, too?" Teddy asked.

Troy thought for a minute. "I tell you what, guys. Give me a little more time. I'll be better prepared to help you real soon. For now, just think about what your business would be if it were perfect, including how much profit you want to make. Seriously. Exactly. And be realistic. Think about it. For now, I gotta' go." Troy got up and made for the door.

"Thanks," Phil called out.

"No problem. There's a lot more, too," Troy added, as he exited into the parking lot.

As Troy pulled out of the driveway, he was stopped by a black truck pulling a 25 foot long trailer with an orange tractor on the back of it. He had to back up to let the Spiders Landscaping truck swing into the lot. Troy and Billy locked eyes for a brief moment.

"I can't waste time thinking about that… guy." Troy finished his sentence out loud.

"Good morning!" Troy said to Sandra and Kara.

"Troy, you're not going to believe it!" Sandra said excitedly. "Harmon sold another job already!"

"Another one?" Troy asked.

"Yeah. It's a small one, $6,200, and it wasn't even a lead I got him; he got this lead on his own!"

"Holy cow! That is fantastic!" Troy said.

"He said he's bringing in the contract later today," Sandra said.

"Great. How's Max doing?"

"No sales yet. He seems to be doing okay, I guess," Sandra told him.

"Well, I think we're on our way!" Troy declared.

"It looks that way," Sandra agreed, with Kara smiling behind her.

As Troy turned the corner from the hall to his office, and flipped the light on, he was startled to see Cy sitting there in his guest chair. "Good morning, Cy. It's great to see you!" Troy said, as he closed the door. "I didn't know if I'd see you again."

"Me, neither," Cy replied. Troy looked puzzled at Cy's response, as he offered Cy coffee.

"Coffee would be heaven," Cy said, as Troy walked out of the office. "Well, not exactly heaven," Cy spoke to himself out loud.

Troy came back with two coffees in his hands and shut the door again. "Well, Cy, I have to tell you. I'm on my way," he said.

Cy knew what Troy was talking about. "To your ideal future?"

"Yes!" Troy said.

"You sound excited. Tell me what you've done so far," Cy asked, as he settled in his chair, palming the warm coffee mug.

"Well, I took your advice and I'm fixing my business so I can do better and make money with what I have, without spending a lot…" Troy looked up and added, "without spending ANY money."

"Very good, young man. What did you do?"

"I had to let my salesman go. It was something I knew I had to do for a long time, but I didn't think I could get a good replacement. But he wasn't getting the results so… I replaced him with two superstars. Well, one is a superstar – he sold two jobs in two days with one lead!"

"Wow. That's great, Troy. So what did you learn that you won't forget?"

"That I can't compromise with salespeople – I need the best," Troy replied proudly.

"And?" Cy asked.

"Well, that it's amazing what talent is out there if you only look and talk to enough people. And I learned from my new friend Mike to interview multiple times, and at a meal," Troy said, reporting his progress proudly.

"I am proud of your follow-through and ability to take advice and act on it decisively," Cy told him. "What else did you do?"

Troy continued, “I made a production management system. It’s unique. I got advice from a few guys, but then added some new dimensions. Want to hear it?”

“Of course,” Cy said, Troy’s enthusiasm rubbing off on him.

“Okay, we’re calling it Bobber.”

“Bobber?” Cy asked, laughing a little.

“Yeah. It stands for ‘Best Outcome, Best Reporting’. What happens is, on every job we have a lead man running the job on site. And what we do is, at the end of each day we have him take pictures of each job with his phone, of what the crew and subs did that day, and email the photos in with a brief description of what they accomplished. Then we ask him to say what the best outcome for the next day would be – like a goal for what to shoot for the next day.”

“Sounds interesting,” Cy said.

“Well, there’s more. In the office, the production manager reviews the photos and Best Outcome goals for the next day, and prints and posts them on a huge bulletin board in the office. Each lead man’s photo is on the board over his job. They know their progress is up there for all to see, including the photos of their work. That’s a big motivator, when they know everyone else in the company can see what they’re doing. We also set goals for how long the job should take at the start, and we track how they do against that. If they finish sooner, they get a bonus,” Troy explained.

“I like it,” Cy said.

Troy continued, “And another part of it is that we pay a percentage of the job, always giving the crew a bonus if they come in under that – so they have incentive to do their best and to manage the subs on their job, too. Of course, the customer has to be happy with the job for the crew to get any bonus. And they're also responsible for emailing in any material they'll need, two days in advance. Custom materials are ordered before the job starts."

Cy nodded. "Sounds like the fundamentals are there."

Troy continued, "With our 'Bobber' production system, the crews are almost self managed. The production or office staff will call the customer every day to report what's going on, to see if the customer has any questions or concerns, and if they're happy. If there are any problems from the customer's point of view, or the lead man's point of view, the production manager goes out to the job site to straighten it out. And one production manager can manage twice as many jobs this way, by seeing what's going on without visiting the job sites each day."

Cy looked directly at Troy. "Young man, you have made extraordinary progress! You've grasped the idea of creating a system that will work inside your business, that you can easily teach everyone, and plug anyone into. Besides that, this system unlocks basic human desires to look good among our peers, and to take responsibility for what we're doing. I'm very impressed with you, Troy," Cy said, serious as he could be.

Troy beamed. "Really?"

"Really," Cy said, nodding his head.

"Remember when I told you it's 'how you think' that will make all the difference in your business?"

"Yes," Troy replied.

"Well, you're thinking right. Of course, you'll have to make adjustments, and some things might not work out the way you thought; but if you stay flexible, and approach the snags with the same creativity, you'll do great," Cy told his student.

"Well, I had a lot of help. Freddie and I did it together," Troy admitted.

"Even better. That you involved your team makes them buy in, and have input. They won't fight the new system if they had a part in creating it. So that was brilliant on your part!" Cy credited.

"Well, I wanted to tap into what my team knew," Troy told him.

"Great. Still, you were the leader, and without your initiative and vision, nothing would have happened. So you are responsible. But hear this; you have to give Freddie and the others credit for doing it. Even though you know your role, give away the credit. It's amazing what you can accomplish if you don't care who gets the credit."

Cy was speaking to a new man. "I will. I'll celebrate their work and tell others inside and outside the company about what they created," Troy promised.

"I think I'm going to have *everyone* design their own systems," Troy thought out loud.

Cy grimaced a bit and said, "Well, that sounds noble. But remember, all people are not equal performers because they're not all equal thinkers. You have to get great people, but don't expect them to have equal abilities. They won't be equal. Delegating these creative tasks that mean so much to the future of your business can be helpful for extracting what others know; but in the end, you are responsible for making it work."

"Yeah, I guess you're right. I've been lucky so far. Freddie and Sandra and Kara are my best people. I got your point," Troy said with now tempered enthusiasm.

"Let me ask you — how do you know you'll make any money on the jobs you sell?" Cy asked.

"What do you mean?" Troy asked.

"Well, if you aren't making any money now, and you want to make 12 percent, how is that going to happen?" Troy thought about Cy's question, but didn't quite know what to say.

"When you're in business and want to make a profit, you have to buy low and sell high. In your case, you are buying labor and materials and your overhead at one price, and wanting to sell them for 12 percent more than that. Right?" Cy asked. Troy nodded.

Cy told him, "Well, there are two sides of the equation – the prices you buy for, and the prices you sell for. You have to pay attention to both sides, and there has to be a spread between them."

"I see what you're saying. So I have to raise my prices and lower my costs, right?" Troy asked.

"Yes. And it sounds simple. But the market won't let you just do whatever you want with costs and prices."

"What do you mean?" Troy asked.

"Well, you can't just jack up your prices to make a profit on top of inflated costs. If your prices are too high, what happens?" Cy quizzed.

"Then my customers won't hire me and they'll take a lower bid instead," Troy answered.

"There are value issues, but right. For the most part, the higher your prices, relative to what else is available, the less people will buy."

"So I have to reduce my costs as low as possible then, right?' Troy asked.

"That's another element, and yes, you need to pay attention to your costs. If you can buy the same materials and services for less, then it's better, of course. But in your business you have a lot of labor. What happens if you don't pay people much?" Cy asked.

"Well, they may leave and go work somewhere else. Especially the best people," Troy replied.

"Right. And you need great people, especially in certain positions."

"Right," Troy agreed.

"On the other hand, you can start with good people who have potential, who don't come to you off of another higher paying job, and don't ask for a very high salary, and put them in a healthy, productive work environment with other good people, and have them work within a system that produces great results," Cy guided.

He added, "Troy, you have to watch both sides. What you pay, and what you charge. What your business is doing is processing labor, materials and outside services, and combining them efficiently to create something more valuable, and selling it to the customer. The more efficient your business is at that, the more competitive and profitable you'll be."

"Whew," Troy said, blinking hard and shaking his head. "You got me going again. You're right, Cy." Troy reached into his bag and pulled out the Blue Book. Cy watched Troy make notes as he finished his coffee. Troy wrote and wrote.

Just then, Sandra pushed the door open. Troy whirled to see her, and looked back at his desk chair. It was empty.

"I'm sorry to bother you with this, but Harmon just called," she said.

"Another job?" Troy asked.

"No, Troy," she said, hesitating. Troy could see something was wrong. "He quit."

"What?"

"He said he had to move to Canada, and said he'd call and explain later, and that he was very sorry because he wanted to work here, but he couldn't. That's all he said on the voice mail," Sandra finished solemnly. Troy's face crumpled along with his spirit.

As Troy pulled onto the Kaspian's street, a black truck with a big trailer was coming the other way. It was the same Spiders truck he had seen that morning, with the tractor on the trailer. The rig stopped in front of a house four doors up the hill from the Kaspian's home. When Troy pulled up, he forgot about the truck as he paused in front of his customer's home and admired the work his crew had done. They had transformed this home, and it looked great.

As he slowly pulled into the driveway, he thought about when he had walked into this very same driveway and saw the concrete truck, and about how he had blown up at Danny. He shook the bad memory off, and admired how Freddie had made the job come out great. But Danny was gone. And so was Harmon. Troy had thought he was making progress a few hours ago, but now… it didn't look good. He shook it off again, and went inside to get a testimonial from Mrs. Kaspian, and take pictures.

"Thank you very much, Mrs. Kaspian. Call me anytime if you need anything at all. And we appreciate referrals."

"Thank you, Troy," Mrs. Kaspian said, and she showed Troy out, holding her little dog in her arm.

As Troy got in his truck, his cell phone rang. "Troy." It was Sandra, and she sounded upset.

"What's wrong?"

"Troy," she hesitated. "That $27,000 job… they cancelled." She told him like she didn't want to.

"What? Why?"

"They wouldn't say. They just said they wanted to talk to Harmon, but I can't get a hold of him."

"Ohhh…" Troy said, devastated. "Once Dingman's job is done, and that other little one, we're out of work," he said.

"I know, Troy. I know. But that's not all." Troy was quiet and waited for her next piece of news. "Max Brady quit."

"What? Both guys quit in one day?"

"He said we didn't have enough for him to work with – that our brochures from the lumber yard weren't enough for him to do his thing."

"Ohhhhhhh," Troy groaned. "Is that it?"

"I sure as hell hope so," she said, feeling his pain. Sandra never used curse words, so "hell" was pretty strong for her. Troy hung up his phone and dropped his head on the steering wheel. There he sat for a long while, thinking about how he now had no salesmen, no work and few leads, how Piper and Spiders had conspired against him, how he lost Danny, and how all of a sudden he was going backwards.

Tap, tap. Troy picked his head up off the steering wheel. His forehead was resting there so long it left a temporary red mark. It was Mrs. Kaspian. He turned the key on and put the window down. "Are you okay?" she asked.

"Yea, I just got some bad news," he told her.

"Is everything okay?"

Troy looked at her, and nearly cracked. He took a breath. "Yep. Yep. I was just thinking. But thanks."

"Okay, you sure now?" she said, not convinced by what she was seeing.

Troy started his truck. "Absolutely. Thanks." He pulled back out of the driveway, turned into the street and put the truck in drive.

Just then, Troy heard a man yell. Then he heard a woman's voice yell, "Oh my God!" Troy looked out the driver's window to see Mrs. Kaspian standing in her driveway, looking up the street in horror. Troy heard a loud scratching noise up the street in front of him. The trailer with the tractor had unhitched from the truck, and was rolling down the hill backwards, by itself.

A man in a black shirt ran after it, but it was picking up speed as it rolled down the hill, and there was nothing he could do if he caught it anyway. "Oh my God!" Mrs. Kaspian yelled again, pointing across the street. Troy looked to his right. The trailer was headed toward a house with a porch.

Things happened fast, but Troy began to see in slow motion. The porch, people on it, kids playing in the yard in front of the porch, a bend in the road, the giant runaway trailer coming with a big tractor on it, a wooden fence in front of the house, and screaming.

The trailer jumped the curb. Troy mashed the gas pedal to the floor. The trailer crashed through the wooden fence at the corner of the yard, heading straight for the porch and the people. Troy turned the wheel right and smashed his truck through the wooden fence in the middle of the yard, heading at an angle towards the speeding hulk. Troy braced himself as the trailer with the tractor on it collided with his truck. Crunching metal... orange and yellow steel… then it all went black.

Chapter 16

Assessing the Damage

"Oh, Troy," Karissa called, as Troy opened his eyes. She started to cry. "Can you hear me? Are you okay, baby?"

Troy looked around him. He was in the hospital. There was a window. It was night. His parents and Karissa's parents approached the bed. They were all tearing. There were cords and tubes and wires.

Troy smiled at her. He wiggled his fingers. Then his toes. He moved his arms a little, and then his legs. "Owww," he said when he moved his left leg. "I think I am." He tried to shift up in bed a little, but realized his shoulder and hip on his left side were hurting.

A nurse appeared. "Stay there," the nurse said, grabbing his wrist and looking at her watch.

"What happened?" Troy asked. Karissa tried to speak, but she couldn't get any words out without crying.

"You saved two kids' lives, Troy," his mother said to him, and she began to cry.

"I did?" Troy said weakly.

"You were in an accident. Do you remember?" asked his father. Troy tried to remember, but it was faint.

"Was there a trailer involved?" he asked.

"Yes," his Dad told him.

Troy winced as he tried to move again. "Just rest," the nurse told him. Karissa held his hand. Minutes passed as they were all quiet.

The nurse left the room.

"Is anything broken?" Troy asked.

"No, thank God. The corner of the trailer frame came through the driver's door and pinned your legs in the truck. They had to cut you out," his father said. Everyone talked quietly.

"The fireman said that it could have been much worse. The trailer frame could have broken both of your legs, but something got between the sharp corner of the frame and your legs that spread the load out," his father told him. "So you just have bad bruises on your legs and hip and shoulder."

They all stood around his bed quietly. Karissa's mother passed around a tissue box. "What time is it?" Troy whispered.

"It's 2:30 in the morning" Karissa said. "Mrs. Kaspian just left an hour ago. And Freddie and Teddy and Phil and Sandra and Kara and the Morey's – the whole waiting room was full last time I was out there."

Seconds passed in the quiet room. "Who are the Morey's?" Troy asked.

"They live in the house where the accident happened," Karissa explained slowly. "Mrs. Morey's parents were on the front porch watching the Morey's two children while they were at work." Karissa saw she needed to give Troy time to process what she was saying. "Do you remember?"

"I think so," Troy said, not sure.

"Let me go tell who's left in the waiting room that Troy woke up," Troy's father said.

"Dad," Troy stopped him before he left. "What was it?"

"What was what, son?"

"What got between my leg and the trailer?"

"The fireman said it was a book. A blue book."

Troy woke up to a doctor checking him. Light streamed through the window. Karissa stood next to the bed, looking tired. She grabbed his hand. "Hi," she said softly.

"Hi," he said.

"How do you feel?"

"I'm gonna' to be okay," he said, with his voice lifting a bit, showing new energy. "When can I go home, doc?"

"Today," the doctor replied. "There is nothing wrong except a few bad bruises, and you had a concussion. So we'll keep you until this afternoon, but then I see no reason to keep you."

"Sweet," Troy said.

Karissa was smiling. "The kids are coming with my mother. They should be here any minute." Just then Troy's parents walked in.

"I'm outta here today," Troy told them.

"Really? That's great!" his father said. "Take a look at this." His father held up the morning newspaper. "It's all over the TV, the radio, and the newspapers."

Troy reached for the paper. There was a huge photo of his mangled truck. You could still see the lettering on the truck – "Troy Builders, 478-671-5566." The trailer had skewered the truck on the driver's side. The tractor was on its side on top of Troy's truck. The words "Spiders Landscaping" could be seen on the side of the trailer frame. The front porch of the Morey's house was just 10 feet behind the truck.

"Holy… smokes…" Troy said, staring at the photo.

The headline read, "HERO SAVES 4 LIVES, RISKING HIS OWN." Troy began to read the story.

"A runaway trailer loaded with a tractor streaked down a hill towards a Mission St. home where two young children played in their front yard, while their grandparents watched from the front porch. 'It was the scariest moment of my life,' Diane Kaspian said. 'I saw the whole thing from right across the street.'

'I was never so scared in all my life,' Margaret McKensey said. 'We were watching in horror as the trailer smashed through the fence and came right at the four of us. I thought we were all going to die right there. And then, like a streak from heaven, this blue pickup truck comes from nowhere and intercepts the trailer. There was a huge crash, and I looked down at the kids, and they were laying on the ground just three feet from where the wreckage came to rest.'

The children, Angela Morey, 4, and Douglas Morey, 6, and their grandparents, Margaret and Daniel McKensey, were unhurt in the incident. The pickup truck was driven by Troy Becker of Troy Builders, who was visiting one of his customers, Diane Kaspian, across the street. 'He was there at that moment, and took action. Without any hesitation he drove his truck through that fence and put it between this speeding trailer with a tractor on it, and those kids. I witnessed a miracle like I have never seen in my life. Troy Becker is a hero,' Mrs. Kaspian, said, visibly moved.

The trailer, owned by Spiders Landscaping, was unhitched on a hill by an employee. The employee, Jake Mulrooney, said he forgot to chock the wheels of the trailer. As it started rolling, the hill got steeper and the trailer picked up speed. 'I am so sorry. I nearly killed people, and I can't say I am sorry enough. Troy Becker saved four lives, and mine, in five seconds,' Mulrooney said.

Paramedics and firemen worked for 45 minutes to extract Mr. Becker from the wreckage. First, a tractor had to be removed from the top of Mr. Becker's truck, and then he had to be cut out as his legs were pinned inside. At press time, he remains unconscious at Memorial Hospital."

"Is that what happened?" Troy said.

"That's it. We are so proud of you, son," his mother said. Parts of the incident came back to Troy, but he couldn't remember it clearly.

Karissa's mother poked her head in. "Is he up?" she asked Karissa.

"Oh yeah," she said, showing her mother her relief.

"Should I bring the kids in?" her mother asked. Karissa waved. Troy's three kids walked in, not knowing what to expect.

"Hey guys!" Troy said. "Come on in. Don't worry, it's okay, I'm fine. I'm coming home in a few hours." The kids took turns hugging him.

"I was scared, Daddy," Hannah said.

"It's alright, baby." He hugged her and held her for a long time.

"You have to sit in the wheelchair, sir," the man in white said to Troy.

“But I’m fine. I can walk,” Troy said, as he winced when he stood up.

“Hospital rules.”

“Karissa, do you have all my stuff, my phone and wallet?”

“I got it, don’t worry.”

“Where’s the book?”

“What book?”

“The blue book that was in the truck.”

“Your dad emptied your truck before they finally took it away. I think he has it,” she told him.

Troy took the next day off. Sandra called to ask if he was okay, and she said she’d tell Freddie and the others as much.

“I have your things,” his Dad called out, as he came into the living room. He carried a garbage bag of stuff from the truck. Troy opened it and rifled through it. He pulled out what he was looking for. It was the blue journal. He turned it over to find a triangle shaped dent in the middle of the back cover. He clutched the book and closed his eyes.

“Thank you,” he said solemnly, like he was talking to someone who wasn’t in the room.

“Is it okay if I go shopping with the girls? Are you okay?” Karissa asked.

“I’m fine. Go ahead,” Troy told her.

“Okay, I’m taking Hannah and Shelby, and Tarin is upstairs on his computer.”

“Okay, baby.”

“I’ll buy you some Hagen Daas to speed your recovery.”

“That’ll do it!” he said laughing.

Troy sat on the couch and picked up the blue book. He turned it over and stared at the dent for a long while. He opened the book and read his notes from the beginning. As he read, and began to think about his business, all of his problems began to come back into his mind. As he read, he was encouraged by the words, but at the same time troubled that nothing was working for him.

He recalled that he was out of work, had no salesmen, and few new prospects. The pain in his hip, shoulder and leg made it hard to think positively. Soon, he’d be out of business, he thought.

He continued reading for a long while. When he got to where he had made his last notes, he flipped the page, expecting it to be empty. Instead, he saw new words. It wasn’t his handwriting, but the same writing as the “Think Daily” passage.

It read, “Anyone can hold the helm when the seas are calm. Never give up. Ever.”

Troy lay down on the couch with the book on his chest, thinking about the words. He fell asleep.

A voice woke him.

“Daddy, we got your favorite,” Hannah said. “Vanilla Swiss Almond.” She had a small container of ice cream in her hand and a spoon.

“Aww, thank you, baby.”

Chapter 17

Grim Reality

Troy made his way to the spare company pick-up truck that Freddie had delivered to his driveway the day before. It was 15 years old, and it rattled and squeaked. It smoked when you started it, until the struggling engine was warm. The faded body was textured with the uncaring blows of countless users who didn't own it, and the wheels didn't match. It would have to do until Troy could work it out with the insurance company and get a new truck.

As he pulled into the coffee shop, he saw three black trucks. That bad feeling came over him again, but now it was compounded by the pain in his left side. As he made his way into the door, walking a little slower than usual, he saw that the place was full. In seconds, people noticed him.

"There he is!" a voice said, and then another.

"Hey, it's Troy!" another voice called out. Then the whole place erupted in applause and cheers. Troy stopped and looked around to make sure it was him they were cheering for.

"Great job, Troy!"

"Awesome!" Voices came above the crowd. As the cheers died down, a big man appeared in front of him. It was Billy. He hesitated for a moment. Most of the people in the place knew there was bad blood between the two men, and they were all looking at Troy. They knew Troy had intercepted a Spiders trailer; everyone knew it. As Billy stood in front of Troy, everyone got quiet and watched.

Billy seemed like he wanted to say something, but he couldn't get it out. The big man stood in front of Troy in the middle of the coffee shop and started sobbing. When he could, he began to speak. "In 1987 I had a five year old son… " The tears streamed down Billy's face. "...and he was killed in a car accident…" Billy struggled to breathe. Troy looked up at Billy, feeling his pain.

"If one of my trailers ever killed those kids, I couldn't live with myself… Thank you for what you did. If there is anything I can ever do for you… Thank you. Thank you." Then Billy covered his face with his hands.

Troy put one arm around Billy. "It's okay. Anyone would have done the same thing."

After a long minute, Billy got control of himself and went to an empty booth for a napkin. Everyone was moved by what they had just seen. Not knowing what else to do, Troy approached the counter. Chris was making his coffee. Nobody really knew what to say.

Then a big voice came from the booth area. It was Billy again. "Here's to Troy Becker – my hero!" he said to the whole place, holding up his coffee cup. Everyone cheered again. Billy walked up to the counter. "Chris, whatever Troy orders for a month, is on me."

"Thanks, Billy," Troy said.

"I mean it, Troy. If you ever need help, you call me. I owe you big time." Billy stuck out his hand and Troy shook it.

Billy and his crew walked out while Troy still sat at the window counter. He watched his former nemesis approach his truck. Billy pointed to the door and said something to one of his guys. He pulled the magnetic sign that said "Spiders Remodeling" off the door, and his guy pulled one off the other door, revealing the "Spiders Landscaping" sign. They threw the signs in the back of the truck.

It was a magical morning at the coffee shop.

Troy walked into the office and was greeted by Sandra, Kara, Freddie and his helper, Joe. Sandra hugged him and they all welcomed him back. "You had us worried, man. We didn't know when you would wake up," Freddie said, reliving it. "We were all waiting, and when your Dad came out and said you woke up, we were like, holy… "

"You were there until 2:30 in the morning?" Troy asked amazed.

"We all were. The waiting room was packed. Mr. and Mrs. Kaspian were there, the Morey's were there, Billy was there, and three of his guys, including Danny, Tim the plumber, Teddy and Phil, the news people, and of course all your family."

"Really?"

"Yeah, man. It was a good thing that you did, and people kept cryin' ...it was some scene, lemme' tell you," Freddie said.

Joe added to the conversation. "Dude, you got balls. Your truck was trashed. Someone was watchin' over you."

"Yeah, that's for sure," Troy said, as he showed off some of his purple bruises.

"Ohhh," Kara said.

"Oh, yeah, and Don Singer was there, too," Sandra added.

"Donald Singer from the university?" Troy quizzed.

"Yep."

"What was he doing there?" Troy asked.

"You aren't going to believe this, Troy," Sandra paused.

"What? What?"

Don Singer is Sally Morey's brother. Little Dougie and Angela Morey — those kids are his nephew and niece."

"Whoa," Troy said, shaking his head.

"The newspaper said they were coming by in an hour or so to talk to you," Sandra said.

A feeling came over Troy like he was a lucky man. He chatted with his team for a while more, then turned the conversation over to business.

"Okay, guys. Well, we have to get back to work here. Uhh…you know we are almost out of work, and we have no salespeople now. So I have to get out there again and sell something quick."

"Well, I got a few leads these last few days, so I can schedule them for you," Sandra told him.

"Okay, keep me booked, because our life is on the line here," Troy told her.

The team broke up to go to their daily duties. As Troy turned for his office, he saw the flip chart page on the wall. It read: 1,082 leads, 357 sales, $5 million. It was hard for him to see getting there, when he would be out of work next week.

Sandra came into Troy's office. "Troy. I know you don't need this right now, but we're almost out of money. After payroll this week, I'm about tapped out," she stated sadly. "What are we gonna' do?"

Troy thought for a minute. "When is our next advance on Dingmans?" he asked her.

"Supposed to be on Friday, depending on what Jim gets done between now and then."

"Well, we have to get that check. Tell Freddie, he'll make it happen."

Sandra walked out, leaving Troy sitting at his desk alone. Troy thought to himself, "What now? How are we going to make it through this? One minute everything is going great, and the next, your business is almost dead and so are you." As he unpacked his bag, he saw the blue book.

"Never give up," he said to himself. "Never give up… "

Sandra came around the corner to Troy's doorway. "The newspaper reporter is here," she said.

"Hi, I'm David Spelling from the Post," he said, shaking Troy's hand.

"Hi. Sit down," Troy said.

"That was really something you did," the reporter said. "It was a big story and people want to know more. What made you drive your truck in front of that trailer and risk your life?"

"Ahh, well, ahh... Look, I can't remember. But I am sure that anyone would have done the same thing," Troy said.

"Oh. Well, can you tell me what you thought as you drove through the fence? Did you think your truck would actually stop that trailer, as big as it was with the tractor on it and all?"

Troy paused again. "I can't remember. In fact, I can't remember much from that whole day. I'm sorry." The reported looked disappointed.

"What can you say about saving those kids' lives – and their grandparents' lives, too?" the reported asked.

Troy thought for a moment. "I think God was acting through me. In fact, I know he was."

The reported seemed dissatisfied with the interview, and he wrapped it up and left.

"Honey, I'm going to be late tonight. I have to go on a sales call," Troy told Karissa.

"Are you sure you feel alright?"

"I'm stiff and sore, but I have to go," he told her.

Troy loaded up the clunker pick-up truck with what he needed in order to go on a sales call. He needed to sell something — and quick — and everyone in the company knew it; they were counting on him.

"That was quick," Karissa said, as Troy walked in at 6:45 p.m.

"There was nobody home. They blew me off," Troy said. "I don't feel good. I'm going to bed." As Troy was settling in bed, Karissa came in with some Advil.

"Are you okay?" she asked.

"I'll be fine."

"I know you, Troy, and you're not fine. It's the business, huh?"

He nodded silently. "And my body. It hurts."

"Do you want me to run you a warm bath?" she asked.

"I should, but I can't right now. I just need to sleep. Maybe in the morning, to get me moving." She kissed him, and he fell asleep.

The next day, Troy woke up very stiff and sore, as predicted. He stepped out of the bathtub and looked in the mirror at his bruises; they ran up and down his left side. "Weakness leaving the body," he kidded himself. At least he was well rested.

He visited the last decent size job he had left; the Dingmans. He knew that Freddie and Joe, both his lead men who were now working on the same job, had it under control. He just wanted to see the wheels of his industry in motion, to get some motivation. It worked. The job was going smoothly, and he was proud of it.

Troy asked Sandra to post a job opening for salespeople online again. She was way ahead of him.

"Karissa, I have to do a sales call tonight," he told his wife on the phone. She knew how dire things were, so she wouldn't object.

"Okay. We have Brownies, soccer, and homework tonight," she told him.

"Good luck. I love you," he said.

"Sell it," she encouraged.

It was 9:45 p.m. as Troy walked into the house. Shelby was sleeping, Hannah was in bed, and Tarin was finishing his homework. "Hey, buddy," he said.

"Hi Dad," Tarin said, looking up.

"How was your day?" Troy asked.

"Bad."

"Why?"

"I had school," Tarin said. Tarin was a great student, but not a big fan of school. He always said his day was bad when it was a school day.

"Every day is a blessing, son," Troy said, thinking about his accident.

"Dad, I was thinking…"

"What's that?"

"Well, you know your 'accident,' right?"

"Yeah."

"Well, why do they call it an accident if you did it on purpose?"

Troy laughed. "I guess you got a point, buddy."

Karissa came into the room. "How'd your appointment go?"

Troy sighed. "It's a big job. I gotta' check some costs tomorrow and then get them the proposal. But they need financing, so then I have to try to get them approved if they want to go ahead with it," he said. She knew that meant there was no sale yet, and Troy was one day closer to running out of work.

The next day, Troy went right to work. He enlisted the help of Sandra and Kara to help him get the proposal together from the night before. He asked Sandra to book him two appointments, if she could, for that afternoon. She did. The first customer just wanted her porch railing looked at – it was loose. She was a nice enough lady, and Troy made friends with her. He fixed her railing on the spot in five minutes – no charge.

"I'm dead," Troy said, as he got back in the clunker truck. He called the next appointment, to see if he could show up early.

"Thanks so much for coming out, Troy," the homeowner said to him. "We're going to be getting a few more estimates."

"When?" Troy asked.

"Later this month, probably."

Troy drove home, totally discouraged.

Friday came and Troy showed up at the office early. He saw one sales appointment booked for him at 4 p.m. Troy's cell phone rang. It was Karissa. "The Morey's want to come over tonight at six to see you."

"Okay," Troy said, feeling a little uncomfortable, but not knowing why.

When Sandra came in, Troy asked her if they had received the check from Mr. Dingman yet.

"Not yet. I am hoping to get it at the end of the day because I have to send these out," she said, holding up a stack of envelopes stamped and ready to go. "What about the lead from Wednesday?"

Troy answered, "I called and they said the proposal looks good, and they were going to think about it for a few days and let us know next week."

The both of them knew they were in deep trouble.

"What is this lead that is booked for 4 p.m.?" Troy asked Sandra.

"They saw your truck twisted up on the front page of the paper and they called. They said they waited a few days. The first thing she wanted to know was if you were alive and still working. I told her you were, and then she said she wanted Troy himself to come out and look at her job."

Troy was surprised. "That's a funny way for us to advertise, but it's free! We'll take it!" he told her.

"Yes, we will!" she said.

Troy went through his old résumés from when he was hiring a salesman earlier in the month. He saw his notes on each one. No. No. No way. Not even close. No. Then he found one he had forgotten about. He had written "#3 pick" on top of Todd Runkin's job resume. Troy picked up the phone and called. Nobody picked up, so he left a message for Todd to call.

Troy felt lost. There was no work to do. No money to advertise or pay bills with, no leads to run until 4 p.m. It seemed the business was disappearing each day. Troy tried to think positively, but it was difficult. All his hopes hung on the 4 p.m. appointment.

Sandra came to deliver a blow before the weekend. "Your 4:00 called to reschedule for next week," she said.

He sat there, temporarily paralyzed. "Now what?" he thought. It seemed there was nothing else to do. "Sandra," Troy called as she left his office doorway.

"Yeah," she came back.

"Did we get the check from the Dingmans?"

"No. Freddie called and said Mr. Dingman told him he wouldn't be home on time tonight, so he'll check out what we did on the weekend. If everything is okay, he'll give Freddie a check on Monday."

Troy deflated even more. “Thanks.”

Troy was depressed. When he pulled the old truck into his driveway at 6 p.m., a car pulled in right behind him. “The Morey’s,” he said to himself. He had forgotten, and knew this would interrupt his pity party.

Karissa came out of the front door to meet Troy on the porch; and the Morey’s, the Morey’s two parents, and their two children got out and assembled before approaching the front of the house. As they got to the porch, Sally Morey approached Troy and involuntarily grabbed him and cried on his shoulder. She didn’t have to say anything.

After several long moments, Tom Morey said, “I think she’s trying to say thank you.”

Sally parted with Troy’s shoulder and tried to speak. She looked right at Troy at close range, tears filling her eyes and streaming down her cheeks. “You saved my babies, and I don’t know how I can ever thank you.”

Troy looked at her, and then at the two kids. They looked precious and sweet. Troy thought about his own kids, and his eyes welled up. “I would do it again,” he said.

Once the emotion had burned off a bit, the families introduced themselves to one another and talked a little about the accident. “Why don’t we go inside and have coffee?” Karissa said. As they filed inside, Karissa suggested to Shelby and Hannah that they take Dougie and Angela to play.

“Is it okay?” she asked Sally.

“Yes, of course.”

The Morey’s told Troy repeatedly how grateful they were. And

Margaret and Daniel talked about how the incident had unfolded from their vantage point on the porch. It was emotional at times. Everyone was quite convinced that they would have had four deaths in their family, had it not been for Troy. As Troy listened, he began to feel good, despite his business problems.

"God bless you," Margaret said to Troy, as she stepped off the porch to leave later that evening. Standing next to his wife and children on the porch, he said to himself, "He has."

On Saturday, Troy spent the day with his kids. He tried not to think about his business, and he tried not to think about the accident. He called Karissa's mom and asked her if she could come over and watch the kids, so he could surprise Karissa by taking her out to dinner. When the thought crept into his mind that it may be the last dinner they could ever afford, he laughed out loud. It was one of those comical moments that only the creator could find funny, and he laughed on and off about it for several minutes.

When Karissa came home, he told her about his reservations. Karissa was excited, because she hadn't been on a date with Troy in… well, she couldn't remember when. "Look at this," she said, handing him the newspaper. On the bottom of the front page of the Saturday paper was a follow-up article about the accident. "Modest hero can hardly remember his moment of bravery."

Troy read the article. "More free advertising," he told Karissa.

Whauh... whauh…. whut. "Can you believe it?" Troy said. Karissa's minivan, the primary mode of family transportation, wouldn't start. They sat there in the minivan in the driveway, all dressed up. He tried it again. Whauhhht. The vehicle surrendered. Dead. They sat in silence for a few seconds. And then Troy started laughing. He laughed harder and harder. Then Karissa started laughing. They got out, looked at the jalopy pick-up truck, and got in. They had more fun together that night, than they'd had in years.

That night, Troy dreamed. At least he thought it was a dream. He heard a voice speaking to him. "When you come to the edge of the light, and you are going into the darkness, have faith; you will either find something solid to stand on, or you will learn to fly."

Chapter 18

A Brand New Day

That morning, Troy slept in again. His body was healing now. He woke up and brushed his teeth. He noticed that his bruises were turning yellow and all kinds of colors now, and getting better. He felt better in body and spirit. He thought about his business problems, but now he did not feel defeated; instead, he felt like he was going to fight. He had the energy.

He opened up his blue journal to review his notes. "Funny how you read the same thing and it means something different each time," Troy said to himself. When he got to the end of his notes, he flipped the page, and saw more words that had not been written by him. They read, "When the man is all together, his world is altogether." He laid on the words for a long while.

He hatched a plan for Monday, and he wrote it all down. By the end of the day, he was ready.

On Monday, Troy went to work early and got his thoughts together. When Sandra and Kara came in, he whirred into action. He saw that Sandra was a bit tentative, not knowing what to expect. But very soon she saw that her boss had energy and enthusiasm, and this gave her hope.

"We need to get the check from the Dingman's today. Right?"

"Right," Sandra said.

Kara called out, "There are a LOT of messages on the voice mail this morning."

"Well, let's see what they are," Troy said, as Kara began playing them and writing them down on paper.

As Sandra and Troy talked, they could overhear the messages Kara played on speaker phone. "I'm going to call that $27,000 job that Harmon sold, and try to get it back; and we're going to hire a salesman in the next few days. And I'm going to close a sale myself by tomorrow. And then we need to get a marketing person, even if it's part time, because we need leads," Troy told Sandra.

"Hi, this is Harmon." Troy and Sandra could hear the voice mail playing, and they stopped talking to listen as they approached Kara's desk. "I want to apologize for leaving so suddenly. My wife's mother got sick all of a sudden in Canada, and we had to leave to see her quickly. We thought that we'd have to move to Canada to take care of her, but my wife's sister from Oregon is going to move there instead of us. She's stable now and I'm back. I liked you folks, and I know we can get things going pretty well, so if you want me, I'd be happy to get back in action right away."

The three of them couldn't wait to celebrate, but they wanted to stay quiet until the message was over. "Oh, and on that big $27,000 job, I called to follow up and they told me they cancelled. But I went out there this weekend and I straightened it all out with them. They just needed some hand holding, that's all. So it's back on. They want to get started right away. Please call me as soon as you can. You have my cell number. Thanks."

"Oh yes!" Sandra said. Troy laughed in relief and pleasure.

Kara said, "Well, that's great! And there are 12 more messages!"

Troy went to call Harmon right away. They firmed up the new job, for a Mr. and Mrs. Baker, and made arrangements for Harmon to get started selling again right away. When Troy came out, Kara gave him a summary of the phone messages.

"Listen to this, Troy!" Kara started, as she looked at her list of messages. "Mr. Dingman left a message. He has the check for us and said he was very happy with how the job came out. We had six people call about the sales job, who want interviews. Two people called about the accident just to thank you for what you did, and three people saw you in the news and wanted to call about it, and want estimates now."

"Were gonna' be okay," Troy whispered to himself, as Kara sat beaming. "Well, let's get the sales appointments scheduled first, and the interviews scheduled next."

Sandra was sitting at her desk and called out, "I have emails, Troy, that I think you will like."

"More good news?" Troy asked.

"Two salespeople want job interviews, three people are thanking you for being a hero, Billy from Spiders emailed to thank you again, and … "

"Yeah…" Troy said.

"And your new truck is ready to be picked up!" she said, knowing he'd be happy.

"Great!"

As Troy was walking out the door to pick up his new truck, and visit the Bakers for the first time, a familiar face walked into the office. It was Danny. Troy stopped and smiled at him. He always liked Danny, and hated that he had chased him away. "Hi, Danny. What brings you by?"

"I wanted to apologize," Danny said.

"For what?"

"Well, I don't know. I just feel bad. I knew you didn't like Billy, and I went over there anyway, and I didn't even give you two week's notice or anything," he said.

"It's okay," Troy said. "I've been wanting to apologize to you for yelling at you for the whole concrete mixer incident. You did your best and tried. It was my fault, anyway."

"So, can I have my job back?" Danny asked.

"Really?" Troy asked.

"I quit Spiders last week. Mowing lawns just isn't what I want to do the rest of my life," Danny said.

"I hear ya," Troy said. "Danny, I'd love to have you back. You're a good kid. I just have to make sure I have enough work for you. We're growing the company, and we should be okay. I tell you what. We are starting a new job in a few days, and you can start on that one."

"Deal," Danny said. The two men shook hands.

Then Danny's mood turned down a bit. "Hey, I wanted to tell you that I really respect you for what you did to save those kids and people."

"Thanks, Danny."

"You know… how about I work around the shop and yard cleaning up for a few days until the job starts? You don't even have to pay me," Danny said.

"You don't have to do that, but I'd appreciate it."

"I'll start right now," Danny said, as he walked out the front and around to the back.

Kara gave Troy a ride to the dealership, to pick up his new truck.

“There’s nothing like a brand new truck,” Troy said to himself, sitting behind the wheel, as he took a deep breath through his nose. “I love the smell.”

Troy drove his new truck to his new job – a good sized job for him. Harmon was right. These customers were dream customers. They were very nice and agreeable, and offered a large down payment. They had seen Troy in the paper, and had high regard for him as a result.

“It was a good day, Karissa,” Troy said, as he walked in the house at 5:48 p.m. “Who wants to see Daddy’s new truck?” he called out.

Three small voices answered in unison. “I do!”

The next morning, the team had some excitement. “What a difference a day can make,” Troy told Sandra.

“Yes, either way.”

Harmon came in early to get his leads, and get ready to sell again. He studied the numbers on the wall. Already, he was thinking about scaling up to make the goals. There was something about Harmon that fit right in, and Troy and Sandra and Kara acted as if they had known him for years. He was that kind of guy; seasoned and trustworthy. He wasn’t bold, yet he commanded respect. He was knowledgeable and, most of all, a gentleman.

Troy followed up on his sales calls from the week before. At 2:30 p.m. he walked into the main office and announced, “I sold a nice job!”

“Oh, fantastic!” Sandra said, as she took the paperwork from Troy. “Who do we want to lead this one?”

"Howard can do it. This is perfect for him," Troy said.

On the wall, on a giant bulletin board they had recently put up, was their Bobber system — Best Outcome, Best Reporting. Troy spent a minute standing in front of it, and could see exactly what was going on with the Dingman job, which was finishing, and the Baker job, which was starting, and another small one they had going. There were photos from the day before that Kara had printed, with messages from the guys on site, what materials they were going to need quickly, and their goals for the next day.

Troy wondered how much better it would have been if he and Freddie had thought of the system years earlier.

"I call each customer each day, review where we are, and ask if they have any questions or concerns," Kara said, as she saw Troy looking at the board. "And I get to know what time of day is best to call each customer, and they are starting to look forward to my call. It's working great."

Troy smiled, envisioning what this would be like when they had seven jobs going at once – or more.

"Troy, we got five more leads today, all from the articles in the paper about the accident! When we slow down, you're going to have to do that again!" Sandra joked. The girls laughed as Troy rubbed his left side and faked a groan with a smile.

Chapter 19

Becoming a Leader

The next day, on a Wednesday, Todd Runkin came into the office to meet with Troy. He was Troy's third pick out of the 14 Troy had interviewed for the salesperson job. After talking with him again, for the fourth time, Troy was impressed and felt very comfortable with Todd and his sales abilities. He was the kind of guy that Troy felt comfortable sending out to represent Troy Builders.

"When can you start?" Troy asked.

"Right now," Todd said.

"Okay, let me spend a few hours telling you about our pricing and how we operate, and we can get you a lead this afternoon," Troy said.

Troy felt he was making progress, and had some momentum. When he finished with Todd, and sent him out on his first lead, Troy went back to his office. There sat Cy.

"Cy!" Troy called out with enthusiasm. "I am happy to see you!"

"A lot has happened since I saw you last," Cy said.

Troy slowed his voice. "You were there, weren't you?" Troy asked.

"No, it wasn't me," Cy told him. "Hey, is there coffee on?" Troy was deep in thought. "Coffee?" Cy asked again.

"Oh, yea. You want coffee? Black, right?" Troy asked, snapping out of it. Cy nodded.

"Thanks," Cy said, taking the mug from Troy.

"We were on the edge of disaster last week, Cy. But now

everything seems to have turned around," Troy said, shaking his head like he couldn't believe it.

"Progress is not a smooth line, Troy. When you have a plan, and work on purpose, even setbacks are progress happening."

Troy nodded. "Yeah, but when they are happening, it's hard to believe."

Cy smiled. "I know. But a leader must think clearly in a bad situation, knowing that all opportunities are disguised as unsolvable problems."

"Well, sometimes they are very effectively disguised," Troy said. Both men laughed.

"I can't wait until we accomplish our goal, Cy. Not much has really happened yet, but I can see it now. And when we do it, I'm going to show you… "

Cy cut him off. "Troy, I'm not sure how much longer I'm going to be here," he said, as if he was sad, but looking forward to leaving. Troy looked worried, and puzzled. He was putting together questions to ask Cy along the lines of, "Who are you? Where did you come from? Where are you going?"

Cy heard Troy's thoughts and changed the subject before Troy could get any of those questions out. "Troy, there are a few big holes that need to be filled if you are going to achieve your goals."

That got Troy's attention. "You've been playing manager most of the time. But as you add employees, you must complete your personal transition to that of leader."

Troy looked at him, a bit disappointed. "I thought I was doing good?" Troy said, talking about his personal performance.

"Good or bad can only be determined by what your goals are. Everything counts. An activity either takes you towards your goal, away from it, or it doesn't make any difference at all," Cy told him. Troy sat, wondering what he could be doing better. "The business is a reflection of your thoughts - right?" Cy asked.

"Right," Troy said, recalling some of their earlier conversations.

"So the sooner you make the transition to being an effective leader of a $5 million company, the sooner you will accomplish it." Troy agreed, still a little perplexed.

Cy went on, and Troy could feel another direction-changing message coming on. "Troy, in the process of leading, you must create more leaders in your company. If you are the leader, and you have all followers, then they will be dependent on you, and when you're not there, they will be lost."

"In order to do that, you need to communicate to your people, individually and as a group, and as smaller groups – and communicate clearly and often. As you add people, this will become very important. Especially to the new people. If you don't establish the right expectations, standards of excellence and culture, then they will. And they probably are not going to be the standards and culture that are going to get you to your goals."

Troy got his blue journal out and began to write. Cy gave him some time and waited for Troy to look up again before going on. "Leadership is about mobilizing a great team and igniting their own passions to excel, while accomplishing the goals of your organization. And that's up to you. You are responsible. Everything counts."

Troy made more notes, looked up and nodded.

"Remember when the concrete truck fell through the septic tank?" Cy asked.

"Yeah."

"Well, there was another guy besides Danny and the roofer on that job at the time. Who was that?" Cy asked.

Troy thought for a minute. "Oh, it was Alex. He's a helper," Troy said.

"Would you consider Alex an engaged employee?" Cy asked.

Troy paused. "No," he admitted.

"Why isn't he?" Cy asked.

"Well, he's just a helper… " Troy started to make excuses, and then realized his mistake.

"Can you get excellent work out of a guy like that?" Cy asked.

"No," Troy responded.

"Do you want your customers to see what he is doing or not doing, and witness his work ethic all day at their home?"

"No."

"Whose fault is it that he is there?"

"Mine," Troy admitted. "I hired him in a rush, because one time we needed someone quick. And he was a helper, and we never trained him or expected much out of him."

"Uh huh," Cy said.

"It's a mistake. You're right, Cy. And it's those kinds of guys who bring the others down, and are most likely to steal from me, or make a phony worker's comp claim," Troy said, now coming to his senses. "I'm going to fire him today."

"Maybe firing him is the thing to do, and maybe not. In this case, from what I saw, it probably is. But this is the thing. Everyone has good and bad performance in them. Your job is to create an environment where you can put ordinary people in, and the best in them comes out – and they perform in an extraordinary way," Cy counseled.

"Not everyone is a Freddie," Cy said. "At the same time, do not demand perfection from the untalented. Everyone is different, and has different skills and potential. That's why people don't all make the same amount of money. Putting the right people in the right seats, and getting the best out of them, is your job."

"Troy, you need to develop your people. If you look at someone the way he is, he becomes worse. But if you look at him the way he could be, he becomes better. Nobody rises to low expectations," Cy said.

Troy had that look in his eyes. Cy recognized it – it came when Troy was really processing Cy's words. Cy waited a few moments and went on.

"Now that you're clear about what you want, you must nurture your people, enroll them in the mission, get them involved, communicate often, and get them positioned to get the results you are looking for," Cy continued. "You must work *on* the business, not *in* it, and your employees and the systems they use *are* the business. Get it?"

Troy took a deep breath. "I get it," he said as he began to write more in his journal. Cy could see that many, many pages of notes had been filled in. He smiled while Troy wrote. His student was taking this seriously.

"As a leader, your job is not necessarily to get things done efficiently; it's to get things done effectively. In other words, it's not about doing more things in your day. It's about doing the

RIGHT things each day. You business is a machine that you put marketing dollars into at the top; and if it functions properly, profit should come out of the bottom. Build your machine," Cy instructed.

"Whew," Troy let out. Cy waited for a better hint of what "Whew" meant.

"I got it. I see what you mean. I can do this!" Troy said, as he looked down at his notes and bobbed his head. "Is that it?" he asked.

Cy smiled at him as if to say, "Of course not."

"Remember, your employees don't share the same vision as you. They all have their own lives and hopes and dreams. Sometimes you'll have an employee whose goals are incompatible with yours, and you have to part ways. That's okay. But you have to be a positive, consistent leader for everyone. Find common ground that you can all unite with," Cy said.

"Common ground? What do you mean?"

"Everyone wants to be appreciated. Right?" Cy asked.

Troy thought for a second. "Right."

"So give praise often where it's due, appreciate people and smile. And don't criticize people. And for Heaven's sake, don't gossip or allow gossip in your culture."

"Well, what if someone messes up? How do I straighten it out without criticizing?" Troy asked.

"You call them aside, and ask, 'Could you have done better?' and 'What will you do differently next time?' People who care will beat themselves up enough, and will appreciate you not doing it for them," Cy instructed. "And when you are angry, don't talk to anyone."

Troy thought about Danny. "I got that one."

"You never have to apologize for what you don't say. Right?" Cy asked. Troy nodded as he closed his eyes in regret for a moment.

"Your mood shapes the culture, Troy. You must understand that you are not what you think you are, but what others perceive you to be. The best leaders pay attention to how their communication is landing on people. They learn from it, and make adjustments."

Troy's eyes shifted back and forth as he thought about what his employees thought of him.

Cy said, "Many business owners are poor leaders, and employees leave all the time. This kills their chances of building a great company. There are different styles that can work, but there are three traits that you must have for people to follow you."

Troy was eager to hear what they were, and had a place ready to write them on a page.

"Your employees must feel you care, that you have integrity, and that you are fair," Cy said. Troy wrote it down.

"Now, Troy," Cy said, as if he was changing gears. "You are going to have seven crews working, which means seven lead men, right?"

"Right."

"And you're going to have a sales manager and a production manager, and an office manager. Right?"

"Right," Troy responded.

"Well, you need to build these people into leaders in their own areas of responsibility," Cy said. Then he slowed his voice. "If you hire people who have these qualities of leadership to begin with, then it will be a lot easier for you to make it happen quickly, and make it stick. Yes?" Cy lifted his eyebrows and waited for a thoughtful answer.

Troy got Cy's summary. "Yes," Troy said, slowly and firmly.

Cy's empty coffee cup tapped the desk as he put it down. "You didn't even get to drink your coffee," Cy said, motioning to Troy's full mug.

"Oh, yeah. Well, you don't give me any breaks!" Troy said. They both laughed. "Yuck, cold," Troy said as he tasted it. "I'm going to get a warm one. You want another cup?"

"Ahh, okay, I can have a little more," Cy said.

As Troy went back into the main office, Sandra said, "Troy, Harmon is coming in to see you. He says he has something important to talk to you about, and he needs at least 30 minutes."

"Okay, I'll be here," Troy said, walking away with two cups of coffee.

Sandra said to Kara, "He really needs to stop drinking so much coffee. That's four cups in an hour! I'm going to talk to him about that."

Troy wondered what Harmon wanted to talk about. But then he remembered his conversation with Cy, and looked forward to it. Maybe he wanted to ask about where they would get leads from in the future. "Here you go," Troy said, as he handed the warm mug to Cy.

Cy noticed it was a new mug, and he read what was on the side of it. "Myrtle Beach, South Carolina," he said out loud.

"Yeah, that was our last vacation. We went before we had kids."

"How long ago was that?" Cy asked.

Troy thought, "Ohhh, 14 years ago." Cy let out a little laugh.

"What are you laughing at? It's not funny," Troy said, starting to laugh himself. "Or maybe it is," Troy admitted. "We never had the money. So we'd go on these two-day camping trips, instead. But it was hell with a baby or a toddler, so Karissa started staying home and Tarin and I would go. Still, we had a good time when it didn't rain."

He reflected, "You know, one day I'd like to take the whole family on a nice vacation, to a real place in a real hotel," Troy said.

"Well, that's on your list of reasons, isn't it?" Cy remembered.

"It is," Troy said, with a determined look.

Troy looked at Cy. He knew by now that if there wasn't something important to talk about, that Cy probably wouldn't be here. Troy took a deep breath and let it out, looking disappointed.

"My problem right now, Cy, is that I have two salesmen, and I'm not getting any leads to keep them going, from anywhere other than the press we got from the accident. Some people called because they think I'm a hero, and some probably out of sympathy. It's from an accident that I am getting all these leads," Troy pondered.

"You are where you are, because of who you are, Troy. So is everyone else. Don't discount the attention you got from the accident. The fact is, you did what you did. It was a great thing. Had you not done it, you'd have been a witness," Cy said.
Troy nodded. "But my problem is that next week, these leads that are coming in from that are probably going to stop. And I'll run out of leads."

Cy motioned with his hands. "And… " he said.

"And I need some marketing, right now. I need 1,082 leads a year, which is four and a half a day. I need to hire a marketing manager," Troy concluded.

Cy looked satisfied. "You need more than that, too," Cy said.

"What?" Troy asked.

"We already talked about it, young man. Look at your notes. Ideas are worthless if you don't act on them."

Troy flipped through his book. He kept flipping pages, looking for what Cy meant.

"Let me help you," Cy said, saving Troy from his awkward situation.

"Please," Troy said.

"You hired two salespeople and sent them out there to sell jobs – with what?" Cy asked.

Troy knew now where he was going.

"What did Max Brady say when he•left?" Cy asked.

Troy wondered how Cy knew about Max Brady. "He said we didn't have enough for him to sell with," Troy admitted.

"And you had a fairly high opinion of Max. That's why you hired him, right?"

"Yes. Yes, Cy." He was right.

"If you don't have a marketing image, a competitive advantage, and a strong sales system, then you'll be competing on price," Cy said.

"I'm not going to make my 12 percent profit goal, or have money to invest in my business and people, if I have to be the lowest bidder all the time," Troy said.

Cy was happy that this was all coming back to Troy. "Work on your systems, Troy, because as you grow, little problems can become big ones if they aren't taken care of."

"Troy?" A voice called out. It was Sandra, and she was coming down the hall. Troy got up quickly and met her in the hall. "Troy, Harmon is here," she said.

"Okay," he said. Troy walked out to the main office, leaving Cy behind.

Cy sat in Troy's guest chair. Waiting. He didn't know what for. Either Troy would come back, or the Angel would take him away. He was trying to 'give his gift' as best he could. He wondered when it would be enough. When would he be complete? At the same time, he loved meeting with Troy. He knew he was making a difference. Troy was the kind of person who would follow through and make Cy proud. Cy knew that his advice would make a big difference in the lives of countless employees, customers, and extended family members. He really enjoyed what he was sent back to do, as weird as the circumstances were.

Cy thought about how it would be different, and so rewarding for him, if he was alive, and could meet the other people in Troy's company, and also meet his family. "Why didn't I do this when I was alive?" was still Cy's question. "Why did I have to be sent back like this, my work incomplete?"

Another image came before him. It was the day after his Dad didn't show up for Cy's award presentation at school. "What are you doing home so early? It's only 4 p.m.," his Mom asked his Dad.

"I promised Tommy I'd go to his baseball game," his dad answered. Tommy was Cy's brother, one year older. Cy backed up, away from the scene in the kitchen. A few minutes later, Cy was on the corner to gather the newspapers that were dropped there for his route. His dad rolled through the stop sign on his way to the game. Cy waved, but his Dad didn't notice him.

Chapter 20

A Missing Link

Can we go in your office and talk?" Harmon said.

"Ahhh, hold on one second," Troy said, uneasy. Troy went into his office to tell Cy he had to go, but when he made the right turn into his office, Cy was gone. Troy stood for a moment. He worried that he had just been disrespectful to the man he owed so much to.

Cy was going out of his way to help him. It occurred to Troy that he still hadn't thanked him. His spirit sank for a moment. Then he thought about what Cy had told him — that day, and all the days before. He decided that best way to honor Cy right now was to do his very best at what Cy had told him to do.

"Come on down," Troy called to Harmon, standing in the hall and waving. "Sit down." He motioned to his guest chair.

Troy took a leadership role. "Harmon, I'm counting on you to build a great sales team. If we're going to accomplish our goals, then we need seven great salespeople with talent, who are energized and turned on," Troy told him.

"Well, that's why I'm here," Harmon said, looking like something was wrong.

"What's the matter?" Troy asked.

"I was on a call, and the people had already had three estimates. It was for a roof. And I was the last one in. It turns out, they had a lower price, and went with that instead," Harmon said.

Troy knew what he was talking about, because he had had his share of that happen to him over the last 12 years. "Now, I know how to sell against competition, and I know how to handle a price objection, and I tried," Harmon said.

Troy jumped in. “But you didn’t have much ammunition. Right?”

Harmon looked relieved that Troy already knew what he was getting at. “Right.”

“Harmon, I hear what you’re saying. We need to clarify what makes us unique, and what our sales distinction is. We need to make support materials to show it, and have testimonials and more examples of great projects we’ve done. We need some third party validation, and we have to think about the customer’s shopping experience and how we can make it special for them so we stand out,” Troy explained.

Harmon sat back, wide eyed at what Troy just said. The veteran thought he’d have to educate Troy all the way, and maybe even meet with resistance or ignorance, as he had with previous employers. Instead, he cracked a big smile. “Yes!” he said. “… And we should think about assembling as much of that on a laptop program as we can, using video and neat technology as much as we can.”

“Well, I tell you what,” Troy said. “Why don’t we meet for lunch tomorrow, and we’ll spend a long while working on it? I’ll buy the pizza, and we’ll meet right here.”

“I’ll be here Troy,” Harmon said, as he got up.

“Great,” Troy said.

As Harmon got to Troy’s office door to leave, Troy said, “Hey, Harmon?”

“Yes?”

“Is there any nickname, or short name for Harmon?”

“Well, when I was a kid, they called me Hammy.” They both

laughed. “But I’ve since outgrown it,” Harmon said. They both agreed.

On Thursday morning, Troy walked into the coffee shop at his regular time. Chris was at the counter as usual, and standing in front of the counter was Teddy and a woman who Troy did not know. “A-l-b-a-k-e-r-q-u-e,” Chris said.

“Nope,” the stranger said. Troy approached and leaned against the counter next to Teddy.

“A-l-b-a-q-u-e-r-q-u-e,” Teddy said.

“Almost,” she said.

“What are you guys doing?” Troy asked.

“She is from New Mexico, and somehow we got to spelling the name of the capital,” Chris said playfully.

“A-l-b-u-q-u-e-r-q-u-e,” Troy rattled off.

“Right!” the stranger said.

“You dog!” Teddy said to Troy.

“Helen, this is Troy. He’s a good friend of ours,” Chris told her. “Pleased to meet you,” Helen said, shaking Troy’s hand.

“What brings you here from New Mexico?” Troy asked.

“My husband is a military man and was transferred here. We bought a house nearby. This is literally my third day here, and I was relieved to find this coffee shop. I always went to a place like this in the mornings back home, and I was hoping I could find an equivalent here," she explained.

"Well, you can come here every single morning," Chris laughed. "And lunch and dinner, too," he added. They all laughed.

"Well, nice meeting you. Welcome to town," Troy said, as he and Teddy turned around to sit at the counter at the window. Chris and Helen were still speaking behind Troy and Teddy for a minute, while she waited for her breakfast.

"You don't know anyone looking for a marketing professional, do you?" Helen asked Chris. Teddy started talking to Troy, but he wasn't listening to him. He was tuned in to the conversation behind him.

"I had to leave my old job when we moved, and I'm looking," she told Chris.

"What kind of marketing do you do?" Chris asked.

"I worked at a small company, so I do it all – graphics, networking, advertising and, in recent years, a lot of internet," she explained.

At that, Troy wheeled around and stepped back towards Helen. "Are you kidding me?" Troy asked her.

"What?" she asked, surprised.

"I need to talk to you, right now. Do you have a minute?"

"Well, I have nowhere else to go," she said. Troy excused himself from Teddy and went to a booth with Helen. They talked for over an hour.

"I tell you what. Let me come in and see your business, and I'll give you some advice and ideas. If you like my work, then we can talk about a position. If you don't, then we part friends,"

Helen said. She was smart, well-spoken, and easy to talk to. Troy remembered his conversation about hiring employees too quickly and making mistakes. But her 'try-before-you-buy' offer carried little risk.

Troy remembered his meeting with Harmon at 12 p.m., as he looked at his watch. "Why don't you come in around 3 p.m.?" Troy asked her.

"Okay," she answered.

Then Troy stopped and thought for a moment. "Wait. How about you come in at noon?"

"In just a little while, then? Okay," she said, knowing Troy had something up his sleeve; she was ready for the challenge.

At noon, Helen walked into the office and Troy was up front with Harmon, who had just arrived, to greet her. "Hi, Helen," Troy said, shaking her hand. "This is Sandra, Kara, and Hammy." Troy stopped to watch Harmon's reaction.

"Hammy?" Sandra asked.

"It's a childhood nickname. We can talk about it later," he said smiling. Harmon stuck his hand out to Helen.

"Hi, I'm Hammy," he said, looking over at Troy and going along with it.

"Everyone, this is Helen… I'm sorry, I never got your last name," Troy said.

"Baylor. Helen Baylor."

"Helen just moved here from New Mexico, and she is a marketing professional. Right?" Troy said looking at her.

"Right," Helen said. Sandra, Kara and Harmon all looked surprised and pleased with Troy's announcement that Helen was a marketing professional. They all knew that's what they needed.

"Hammy," Troy said, looking again at Harmon to see if it was okay to call him that.

"Yes, Troy," Harmon said, showing he kind of liked it.

"I thought that we could have our brainstorming session with Helen, who I just met, because sales and marketing are joined at the hip."

"You got that right. Perfect!" Harmon said.

The three of them sat at the table in the main office where Kara and Sandra could see and hear the whole conversation from their desks. Troy started by telling the history of the company, and what their goals were. Then he outlined their strengths and weaknesses. Helen wrote lots of notes. Harmon then explained his ideas about what the sales force would need to be most effective.

Helen listened, and when Troy and Harmon were all talked out, she spoke. "Well, you need a logo, and you need a marketing image graphically, and with a message. And you need a company brochure, and lead generation brochures, and some materials for the salespeople to get their points across. And we should pick some values the company stands for, so I can weave them into the message," she said.

"Integrity and keeping promises," Troy said.

"Okay, those are kind of the same thing, and they are highly valued," she said, as she wrote them down.

Helen continued, "And we need to decide on how we're going to market the company for lead generation. With a limited budget, we'll start with the internet, networking, shows, referrals, and yard signs." Helen rattled off her prescriptions like she knew this stuff cold.

Troy looked over at Sandra to see her approval. Hammy was bobbing his head like he was in a trance. Troy could not believe his good fortune.

Troy heard Cy's voice: "Everything you need is all around you. You just have to tune in."

"And we'll have to take a look at what your trucks look like," Helen said.

"I love you!" Troy said out of his excitement.

Helen felt a little awkward until Sandra said, "Me too!"

Then Harmon said, "Me three!" They shared a laugh.

"I've been thinking," Troy said. "You know the production system we developed?" he asked Sandra and Harmon, motioning to the wall. "Well, that's a big deal. It's unique to us, and ensures customer satisfaction. We should market the heck out of that, and talk about it in our sales process."

Hammy instantly agreed. "Yes, because we use the same roofing and siding as everyone else, or at least they can get it, so we need something like that. That's good," Hammy said.

"Okay, let me go back a step," Helen said. "I'm just thinking about the name of the business here. I don't know how attached you are to it, Troy, but 'Troy Builders' is pretty generic and doesn't really say what we do."

Troy not only agreed, but he picked up on Helen using the word 'we'. "Do I have permission to work on some other ideas?" she asked.

"Absolutely," Troy said.

The team bounced ideas around for nearly three hours. Everyone added to the conversation. Kara suggested some names and taglines. Hammy thought about the competitive advantage, and Sandra talked about their target audience and geography. The team was energized, now that the 'missing link' was filled in.

"Can I visit a job site or two?" Helen asked.

"Just two," Troy joked, "'cause that's all we got right now!" Hammy wanted to go as well.

Troy took them to the Dingman job and they met Freddie. Then he took them to the Baker job and they met Howard and Joe. Then Troy decided to take them by Mrs. Kaspian's. When they pulled up, Troy stopped and stared across the street at the Morey's home. It was the first time he had been back there since. He couldn't remember the accident, but he visualized what it must have been like by looking at the damage.

The fence was smashed through 20 feet wide in two places, with only 15 feet left standing between the gaping holes. The ruts in the yard were deep; it looked like quite a calamity had gone on. Then he noticed the porch, just 10 feet from the ruts in the yard, undamaged. He sat there, just staring at it for a minute, while Hammy and Helen somehow knew to stay quiet.

Troy turned to look at the Kaspian home from the street, and explained what they did there. Helen was glad Troy had Mrs. Kaspian's happy testimonial on video. "But I haven't checked if my video camera survived the accident," Troy said, remembering that his video camera was in the truck at the time of the accident, and trying to remember if his Dad had recovered it.

"What accident?" Helen asked. Troy parked where they could all see the scene, and he explained what they told him had happened.

Helen sat in the passenger side of Troy's truck. She was moved by the story, and wiped her eyes. Just then, Sally Morey came out of the house with her two young children, Dougie and Angela. She hadn't recognized Troy's new truck. They walked to the mailbox, took out its contents, and went back inside.

All three just watched in silence. It was a long minute after the Morey's went in before anyone spoke.

"I have an idea," Hammy said, from the back seat of the extended cab pick-up truck.

"What's that?" Troy said, making a transition in his emotions.

"The Morey's obviously need their fence replaced and their yard fixed. The insurance company is probably settling by now. Why don't we go sell the job? You have a connection you know!" Hammy said, the salesman in him coming out.

"That's a great idea!" he said. Troy sniffled and started to laugh.

Troy tucked the girls into their beds. A bit later he lay in bed with Tarin, and talked to him for a while before putting his light out.

"Karissa?"

"Yeah," she said softly, as she sat on the edge of the bed, tired from her day keeping up with the kids.

"Can I talk to you?"

"Of course. What?"

"I just… I want to say…" Troy didn't know what words to use.

"What?"

"I just want you to know I love you."

"I know that," she said.

"And, I want to apologize."

"For what," she asked.

"For not being the best husband or father that I could be."

"You're a great husband and father," she said.

"No, I haven't been. All those years, working so much, and not being there. All those nights. And all my frustrations. I…"

"It's fine, honey," she consoled.

"No, it's not. I just want it to work out. I just want to make it. For all of us," Troy said, starting to get emotional.

"I know," she said, reaching over and rubbing his back.

"I'm working hard, but it's going to be different. I'm working smarter now. And this won't last forever… I'm going to make it work soon. I promise."

They fell back on the bed together. "I know, baby," she said. She nestled against him, and he held her for a long time. She fell asleep while he stared up at the ceiling. He thought about what to do the next day to keep his promise.

Chapter 21

Moving Forward

It was Friday, and Troy drove to the office, reflecting on what an incredible week it had been so far. Last Friday, he had no work, no salespeople, and few prospects for anything. Now, he had a nice big job to start, some fresh leads, a sales manager, a salesman, a marketing manager – and a new truck that didn't cost him a dime. What a lucky man he was.

"Troy, Mr. Singer from the university wants you to call him," Sandra said.

Troy picked up a phone in the main office.

"Hello, Troy," Mr. Singer said. "You know, Troy, the university has a policy to get three bids on all projects," he started formally. Mr. Singer was a pretty straight, fairly stiff guy. "After careful review of the three bids, and after consideration of the Building Committee's new policy of also considering the capabilities and qualifications of the bidders, I am happy to tell you that we are awarding your firm the job," he said.

"Thank you, sir. I will make sure the Committee is more than happy with its decision," Troy told him.

"And, Mr. Becker, our Committee is looking to reduce the number of contractors we deal with, down to a very small number that we can trust and are comfortable working with. So I will call you as other projects come up, as they often do."

"Oh, wow. Great!" Troy said gratefully.

Then Mr. Singer changed his voice. "Troy, I have to tell you something. Sally Morey is my sister." He paused.

"I heard," Troy said, his voice lower too.

"Those kids are my niece and nephew, and… " Another moment of silence. "I can never thank you enough, Troy. I am eternally grateful."

"Thank you," Troy said sincerely.

"Are you okay?" Sandra said, as Troy hung up the phone.

Troy smiled at her. "I'm more than okay. We just got a big job at the university!" he declared.

Just then Hammy came in. "We got the Morey job!' he shouted.

"What?" Troy said.

"Yeah. It's small, just the fence and some landscaping, but we got it," Hammy said.

"Just like that?" Troy asked.

"Just like that," Hammy said.

Monday morning came, and Troy looked forward to it. At 9 a.m. Helen came in, very excited. "I've been working all weekend, and I want to show you some ideas to see if you like them," she said, as she began unloading things from her portfolio and laying them out on the table. Troy and Sandra converged on the table as Harmon walked in and joined them.

"Well, first," Helen started out, "I've been thinking of a name. I considered how long you've been in business, the name you've had for all that time, what we do, and I came up with this."

The three of them read off a card: "Troy Becker's Exterior Home Transformations." Troy whispered it to himself a few times and smiled.

"I love it," Sandra said.

"I like it because it sounds special, and exclusive and magical," Harmon said.

Helen looked to Troy. "Yeah, it's good. It's really good," he said.

Then she showed him a mock-up of a logo. It was clean and classy. "The name is a bit of a mouthful, so when I did the logo I made the word 'Exterior' smaller. Then I added the tag line, 'We've got an idea for you,' small at the top, and then the words, 'A home you can be proud of' across the bottom. Then we have the services listed – 'Windows, Siding, Roofing, Driveways, Patios, Sidewalks, Stone work, Landscaping, Decks.' "

"There's a lot going on there," Troy said.

"Yes, but this is the full version. For different marketing purposes we could leave out one or both taglines, and/or the list of services. It depends on who our audience is," Helen said. She showed them all the simpler versions. There was an excitement in the room led by Harmon, who had nothing invested in the old name and logo.

Troy and Sandra studied Helen's work for a minute more, and looked at each other for approval.

"It's super!" Troy said. "I love it!"

"Oh great. I'm so glad," Helen said, beaming. "I also made an outline of a brochure, business cards, and a yard sign. But there is one more element we need to put in. Troy, are you available today for about an hour to go to a photography studio?"

"I can make an hour, sure," he said.

"Oh, and it's going to cost about $300 for the photographer. Is that okay?" Helen asked.

Troy looked at Sandra, who nodded reluctantly.

Later that morning, Harmon met with Todd Runkin, the newest salesperson, for a training session. Todd had been out on a few leads and had not sold anything yet. Troy was happy that Harmon took his role as sales manager seriously. Troy popped in on their meeting to give them some information and inspiration, and to go over the company goals.

Next, Troy called Danny. Danny had worked for three days last week with no pay, and had done an impressive job with the shop and yard in back. He even painted the gate and built some extra shelving. Troy was impressed.

"Danny, I want to thank you and compliment you on what you did last week," Troy said. "Can you start on the payroll tomorrow? Great. You'll be a number two man, not a number three. Are you okay with that? Great, we'll see you tomorrow morning! Thanks again, Danny." Troy hung up the phone, feeling good.

Next, Troy stopped back home. Then went to meet Helen at the address she gave him, with the three different colored shirts and the sport coat she had asked him to bring.

"Now stand in front of this green screen and lean like this on the back of this bar stool," the photographer instructed.

"Wait a minute. I'm not going to be in a bar scene, am I?" Troy laughed.

"The stool won't show at all," Helen told him.

For an hour they made Troy pose in many different ways, and then they repeated the whole process many times with the different colored shirts, and with and without the sport coat. Troy didn't know exactly what would come of this, but he thought, "They sure look like they know what they are doing!"

After the photo shoot, Troy met Helen back at the office. "We need to talk about formally hiring you," Troy told her. "Now how much of a salary did you have in mind?"

Troy was a little shocked. He had never had a marketing person on board before, and it would be an expense that he couldn't afford a week ago! In fact, cash flow hadn't really picked up yet, since they only started getting new work a short time ago and hadn't completed any jobs yet.

Yet Troy had faith that Helen's work was just what they needed to get 1,082 leads a year, to feed seven salespeople. They settled on a salary number, and worked out a deal whereby he would pay her 80 percent of her salary, and she would only work four days a week for a while, until things got going. Helen was happy and excited to be at a place where she could make such an impact.

The Tuesday morning sun rose on Troy Becker's Home Transformations. There was a lot to do, but everyone was excited. Versions of the new logo hung on the wall. Troy made some phone calls to get the company name legally changed. Helen asked Troy for the video of Mrs. Kaspian's testimonial. "Oh, yeah, I forgot to look. I'll try to find it tonight," Troy told her.

"Troy, I never thought I'd see this day," Sandra said.

"What day?" Troy asked.

"A lady just called for an estimate, and she said that Billy Trevins from Spiders recommended us highly," she told him, waving a sheet of paper.

Troy thought, "Wow."

"That's fantastic," he said. "He mows a lot of lawns. Maybe we'll get more over time."

Troy met with Freddie to talk about the jobs they had going, and about how the Bobber system was working. Freddie made a few suggestions. "I want to make sure we have the 'before' pictures of each job, so I added that to the system. The lead guy has to take photos before he touches anything. And you can use this for your marketing stuff, too, to show the before and after," he said.

Troy told Freddie, "Fred, we have to get everyone in the organization together in the same place so we can go over how it's going, and what we all need to do as a team. And it's important to recognize people for good work in front of everyone else, and for the guys to get a chance to come into the office and see the board with the photos of their jobs and everyone else's."

Freddie agreed. The two men decided to have companywide meetings every Thursday morning at the office, at 7:30 a.m. There would be coffee, donuts and such, and the meeting would be over by 8:15 a.m. Fifteen minutes would be built in for everyone to talk to each other. Then at 8:30 a.m., it's back to work.

Troy called a couple carpenters he knew who had helpers, to ask if they could come back on and do work for the company soon. His strategy was to have about half of his tradesmen on the payroll full time, and half as subcontractors. This way he'd have flexibility – especially in the winter, when things slowed down.

"Karissa, do you know where the stuff is from my wrecked truck?" Troy asked.

"Your dad had a bag of stuff. I think I saw it in the back hall closet," she said.

Troy found the large shopping bag and rifled through it. There were old maps, papers, a flashlight, some tools, a couple hats and a t-shirt. Finally, in the bottom of the bag, he found the small silver video camera.

Troy sat on the bench in the back hall, among the kids' shoes, coats and umbrellas. He pressed 'rewind,' and when he thought it was enough, he pressed stop. Then he pressed play. He saw Mrs. Kaspian on the small screen.

"They did an excellent job. There are bound to be things that come up on a job like this, and they always took care of it right away. I'm a tough customer at times, and they made me happy."

"Yes," Troy thought, celebrating that the video survived, and that he had found it.

"I'd recommend Troy Builders to anyone."

"Shoot," Troy said, wondering if the company name could be edited somehow.

"Thank you very much, Mrs. Kaspian. Call me anytime if you need anything at all. And we appreciate referrals."

"Thank you, Troy," Mrs. Kaspian said. Troy heard the audio and looked at the screen. He must have forgotten to turn the camera off. He could see the view sideways as he walked down Mrs. Kaspian's front steps. Then he could see the side of his jeans pocket and belt as the camera was on its side on his truck seat.

On the video, Troy heard his cell phone ring. "What's wrong?" he heard himself say. There was a pause. He must have been listening to the caller.

"What? Why?" Another pause. "Ohhh." He heard his side of the phone conversation. "Once Dingman's is done, and that other little one, we're out of work...What? Both guys quit in one day? Ohhhhhhh... Is that it?... I'll see you later."
Troy watched, and started to remember the details of that day.

Then there was a long silence and stillness, as the camera showed the close-up of his right jeans pocket and belt. Troy sat and watched the video, wondering how long it was. He could hear the sounds of tap, tap, tap. He heard keys and the power window.

"Are you okay?" Mrs. Kaspian asked. "Yeah, I just got some bad news."

"Is everything okay?"

"Yep. Yep. I was just thinking. But thanks."

"Okay, you sure now?"

The truck started. "Absolutely. Thanks."

Troy could hear the truck moving. Then in the background he heard a man yell, then Mrs. Kaspian's voice yell, "Oh my God!" Then a scratching noise. "Oh my God," Mrs. Kaspian yelled again, then more yelling.

A chill went up Troy's spine as he sat watching the unaimed camera, and listening to the video.

Tory heard his truck's engine roar and tires squeal, and then the crash of the fence and another crash when his truck blasted through. Then he heard a female voice, and a blur and a crunch of metal and glass breaking, and calamity… and then it went black. Troy sat there wide eyed, looking at the black screen, his heart racing, sweating, and breathing hard.

He swallowed, and rewound the tape. He pressed 'play' and watched again. He rewound it again. It was a female voice, and it looked like a blue flash in front of the lens. He rewound it again. It was his journal flying across the cab. He rewound it again, trying to make out the voice.

"Your work..." he made out. He rewound it again. He finally made out the words amidst the calamity. "Your work's not done."

Chapter 22

A Real Company

Wednesday came, and Troy walked into the coffee shop. Teddy was excited to speak with Troy. "I know what I want," he told Troy.

"Great, Teddy. Let's hear it," Troy said, positioning the stool under himself at the window counter.

"I want three guys and me, and my wife will take care of the office. That's all I need."

"Okay. How much business are you gonna' do?" Troy said, seeing he found the limits of Teddy's vision. They spent 15 minutes talking about it, and Troy headed for the office.

When Troy walked in, there was a big sign across the office. It was a stand-up cutout of Troy, leaning against a sign with their complete logo, tagline, and list of services across the bottom. "Wow!" he said.

"You like?" Helen looked up from the table.

"Dude. That is sweet!" Troy said, borrowing language from his childhood.

Helen wasn't used to being called 'dude,' but she knew she was in the world of contractors now, and she knew Troy was giving her high praise.

"Is this the new sign for our building?" Troy asked, touching the 5-foot-high sign.

"Well, yes, it could be. But I was thinking of these for yard signs," Helen said.

"That's a huge yard sign," Troy told her.

"Well, yes, but nobody in the neighborhood will miss it!" she said.

"That's true," he said.

"They are a little pricey, but I found a guy and talked him into giving us a sweet deal," she said, and followed it up with, "dude." They laughed as Troy continued to marvel over the sign.

Helen showed Troy the new logo on paper, which was very similar to the sign with his image on it. "And I also did this…" she said, as she pointed to the wall. Where the flip chart page was, there was now a graphically beautiful page with their goals on it, that included the new logo in the corner and the words "Integrity" and "We keep our promises" along the bottom.

She showed him mini versions to hand out to each employee, and post around the office and shop. Troy complimented her, and she and Sandra got together to discuss the advertising and marketing they had done in the past.

Troy went into his office and sat down. His desk was reasonably clean, considering he hadn't been at it very much lately. He pulled the blue journal out of his bag and held it in his lap. He stared at the cover. There was something about the gold embossed design that mesmerized him. He opened it somewhere in the middle. He found himself looking at the words, "Think Daily," again. He spent 30 minutes reading his notes from Cy. He had an idea he wanted to write down, so he flipped to find the first blank page. He saw another message, not written by him. It read, "What you dwell on is what you attract."

Troy flipped through all the remaining blank pages, making sure nothing else had been written beforehand that he had missed. How had these messages appeared?

"It must have been Cy," he thought. He read it again. Then Troy forced himself to make an assessment of which parts of his business were in place, and which he would need next. He scribbled on scratch paper and jotted conclusions down in the blue journal, dating his notes.

"Sandra," he called as he walked into the main office. "We need to make a guide booklet for all of our subcontractors. We need to tell them how we operate, train them on how our lead man is in charge of the job, and in charge of them when they are there, and how our Bobber system works. We need to tell them what our standards are, and what we expect from them."

Sandra agreed with him and wrote notes while Troy went on: "I'd like to appoint you as subcontractor and supplier liaison. Is that okay?"

"I do that now, so of course," she said proudly.

"Okay, so you're in charge of subcontractor and supplier relations. Now we need a written system for each group. We need to tell the subs that when we schedule them and they say they will be there, that they must be there with the number of men they say… "

"Uh huh," Sandra said, nodding, as if to expose the subs' tricks.

"And we need to tell them that we get at least two bids on every job, so they keep their pricing sharp." Troy and Sandra wrote down a list of a dozen things they needed from the subs so Troy Becker's Home Transformations could make its goals.

"Once we have this list, we have to have a meeting with all the subs and potential subs at once," Troy said.

"That is exactly what we need," Sandra agreed quickly.

"What about the suppliers? Can we tell them what to do? I mean, what do we put for that?" Sandra asked.

"Uhhh… I don't know. Let me think on that and I'll get to you tomorrow on that," he said.

"Okay. I'll think of some things, too," Sandra added.

"Did Harmon or Todd sell anything else?" Troy asked.

"Harmon said nothing yet, but they have a few good ones they're working on," Sandra informed him.

Troy went back in his office and made a list of everyone who was doing a good or great job. He only had 14 employees, and there were 13 names on the list. He called every one of them, and told them they were doing a good job. He also thanked them, and told them he was looking forward to the future with them on board. It took some time, but he knew he was making a big difference.

Late in the afternoon, Freddie came in on his way home. "Troy, another part of our system needs to be put in place."

"What's that?"

"We have a scrap pile and scrap racks in the back, and it just makes a place for people to put stuff. It piles up and piles up, and nobody takes from there anyway. Let's eliminate the area for scrap. Instead, we send all the good, usable materials back to the supply house. That will save money and eliminate all this mess back there. I mean, Danny just cleaned it and it's a mess again."

Troy looked at Freddie and smiled. The smile turned into a laugh.

"What the hell are you laughing at?" Troy's old friend kidded him.

"It's a great idea. Let's do it," Troy said.

"So, tomorrow's our first meeting. I could tell them?" Freddie asked.

"Yep. You're the production manager. You take charge."

Freddie walked out to his truck, satisfied that he had made a difference, and empowered to think of more good ideas.

Thursday came and Troy looked for Teddy or Phil at the coffee shop, but neither showed up. "Hey man, you all better?" Chris asked Troy.

"Oh yeah, I'm good. I still got a kink in my hip, but it'll be fine," Troy said.

"Yeah man. You been lookin' good lately, brother," Chris said.

Troy knew he was referring more to his attitude than to how he looked. "Thanks, man."

Troy got to the office and saw more cars in the lot than usual. It was the morning of the first Thursday meeting with everyone. "Showtime," Troy said to himself. The employees mulled about the small office, getting coffee and donuts, and admiring the big sign, still there. At 7:30 a.m., everyone was there. There was an excitement in the air.

Troy called the meeting to order. "Okay, everyone. Welcome to our first weekly meeting. I want to make sure you all know each other, so why don't we go around the room and each of you introduce yourselves. Say what you do and how long you've been here, so our new people can get to know you, and you to know them."

Troy was pleased with just this experience alone. He saw each person take pride and ownership of their position just by telling their peers about themselves.

Troy went over the company goals, and painted the picture for everyone of what it would look like. He was very confident and enthusiastic. He and Freddie talked about the Bobber system.

There was some poking fun at the name, but in the end they thought it was playful, and they liked it. Troy went over the values of the company. He talked about integrity, and about keeping promises to each other and to the customer.

He set some action steps for everyone to take in the next week. He turned over the floor to Freddie, who explained the 'no scrap' system. He also told them about putting the big yard signs up, and taking care of them.

Sandra talked about how the lead men were in charge of subs, and the standards they were going to have all subs understand. Helen talked about the marketing, and how they were going to try to get the 1,082 leads as soon as possible.

Hammy invited them all to laugh at his new nickname, resurrected by Troy, and to get it out of their system. They did. Then Hammy told them how he would be building a team of salespeople to handle all the leads that Helen generated, and if they knew any experienced salespeople, to send them in to talk to him. He was getting candidates lined up before he needed them.

"I need everyone involved. You are all valuable, and we need all your ideas and input," Troy told them all. "It may not be easy all the time, and we will have our share of challenges. But I'm willing to try new things to make this a great company we can be proud of. Who's in?"

They all signaled their participation. "Thanks, everyone. We'll continue our meetings each week at 7:30 on Thursdays."

After Troy adjourned the meeting, the employees stepped over to talk to each other. There was laughing, smiles, discussions, and ideas. Troy stepped back and took it all in. It was magical to him. In 12 years, he had never experienced anything like this at Troy Builders.

Now, all of a sudden, he had a real company.

Later that day, Helen showed Troy and Harmon her new company brochure, and the beginnings of a sales book she was working on with Harmon. Things were happening, and happening fast. Troy had professionals in place who knew what to do. Troy realized he didn't have to be the source of all knowledge. He just found and hired the right people, gave them control, and encouraged them.

Hammy interviewed two more candidates before going out on his sales calls. Helen told Troy that the internet was her next important area to work on. Kara heard her and perked up.

Kara asked if she could help on the net, and Helen was glad she volunteered.

"Sandra, I have my ideas for the suppliers. Can we get together on that now?" Troy asked.

"Let's do it," she said, getting out a fresh yellow pad.

"Okay. First, they have to agree to give us their best pricing available," Troy said. "Then they have to tell us if there are product substitutions that can be made to save money. And they have to give us volume discounts as appropriate. And discounts for paying right away."

"If we can ever get there," Sandra said.

"We will," Troy assured her. "And deliveries to us must be complete and on time, and if there are any problems they have to call us right away," he continued.

"I have an idea. They have to see the lead man on the job before they drop the load," Sandra said.

"Great idea. And we can tell them the lead man's name so they can put it on the ticket when we order," Troy added.

"And then don't forget, they have to agree to take back any materials in saleable condition that we don't use," Sandra said.

"Absolutely. Can you type all that up and we'll have a meeting with our suppliers?" Troy asked.

"I will do that, AND I'll have Helen make it look all snazzy with our new logo and stuff, so we can really impress them and they take us seriously!" Sandra added.

"You're the best!" Troy said.

That night, Troy told Karissa all about the day's events, and how he was so excited that things were finally turning around.

Chapter 23

A Long Way To Go

"Where were you yesterday?" Troy asked Teddy at the coffee shop, as Phil looked on.

"I hired this guy last week and he disappeared with my new tile cutter! Friggin' guy!" Teddy said.

"I hate when that happens," Phil said. Troy remembered all those years when stuff like that was a regular occurrence in his own business, but he couldn't see it happening much anymore.

"There is a solution, guys," Troy told them.

"Yeah, it's a 3-part solution. Find him! Kill him! And get my new tile cutter back!" Teddy said. Troy and Phil laughed. Troy decided to let Teddy cool down, and try to help him another day.

It was Friday. "Did you know you have a little geek here?" Helen asked Troy as he walked into the office.

"Geek?"

"It's a compliment to be a geek these days," Helen said, referring to Kara. "This kid knows the internet. She's going to be valuable to us!"

"Wow. I didn't know that," Troy said.

"I'm going to teach her a few things and let her go do a lot of stuff that I'd normally have to do – if that's okay with you, Troy," Helen said.

"Perfect," Troy said, not wanting to stand in his team's way.

"Oh, and I booked a few shows so far, and I'm looking into more of them. I'll have to design a booth, but I have two weeks until the first one," she said.

"Great," Troy replied. Things were happening automatically, it seemed, and Troy marveled at the daily progress unfolding before him.

"Todd sold his first job!" Sandra said, hanging up the phone. "It's a small one, $7,200, but it's a start!"

"Excellent!" Troy said. "I have to go. I'll be back later this afternoon."

"What are you doing here?" Karissa asked, as Troy sat down next to her in the school auditorium for Hannah's school play.

"I'm being Daddy," he said, as the play started. When it was over, Troy found Hannah and gave her a flower and a hug before she had to go back to her classroom. As he got back in his truck, he said to himself, "This is really going to work out."

"It's Mr. Singer calling," Sandra said.

"Hi Mr. Singer," Troy said.

"We'd like you to bid on our lawn care contract, Troy," he said.

Troy thought about how big that must be, and he hesitated for a moment. "Well, we don't do lawn care, Mr. Singer. But I can give you a referral."

"Okay."

"Call Billy Trevins at Spiders Landscaping. He'll be able to handle that."

Troy hung up and called Billy to tell him to expect a call. "Again, thanks Troy," Billy said.

Friday had come to an end, and everyone had gone home except for Sandra and Troy.

"It's the end of the month, Troy," Sandra said.

"What did we have for sales?" Troy asked her.

"Well, we had a rough start, as you know, and most of the sales came in the last two weeks," she said.

"So what was the total?" he asked.

"It was $152,000." Troy pondered the number and compared it to his goal of $416,000 a month.

He said to his trusted office manager, "A long way to go."

Time passed quickly at Troy Becker's Home Transformations. Each team member was engaged in his or her part to build something that had not been there before. Troy continued to guide his team, but not micromanage their individual processes to get the results they needed. In fact, by not being a sales expert or marketing expert, he couldn't tell them exactly what to do – and that suited Hammy and Helen just fine.

Helen's marketing strategy started working, and leads became more plentiful. The internet efforts and strategies put forward by Kara and Helen showed lots of early promise, and Helen doubled her efforts on the web, knowing it was ever more the most important marketing medium, public relations tool, and sales utility.

Sandra took a leadership role in managing subcontractors and suppliers, and continued to develop standards for each. At first the subcontractors and suppliers were taken aback at the company's approach. But they soon found it benefited them, as well as Troy's company, and they appreciated working with a group so committed to excellence. They responded through their actions in dealing with the reborn company.

Harmon hired more salespeople as needed, and the number soon climbed to five, including Harmon. He took his sales development job seriously. Hammy was the kind of guy that didn't want his department to be the weak link; he was fully committed to making the sales department a success.

Troy stuck his head into a sales training meeting, and heard Hammy training. "And most of all, and very importantly for you, Mr. and Mrs. Jones, we have a production management system called 'Best Outcome – Best Reporting.' This ensures you get the best quality, that all your needs and concerns are met as the job goes on, and that the job gets done on time without delays. In addition to our lead man being on the job, taking responsibility, and at your service each day, you will also get a call from the production manager each day, reporting progress, what you can expect the next day, and giving you the opportunity to express any thoughts or concerns you have whatsoever, which are acted upon immediately."

"Doesn't that sound like the unique and special service you're looking for? Well, I want to take a moment now and show you more about how this works. Would that be alright?"

No doubt about it – Hammy was good.

"Troy, I have another idea," Freddie said, coming into the office and going for the water cooler.

"Another idea, Fred? Alright, they've almost always been good. Except for the one about doubling your pay and tripling your vacation," Troy kidded him.

Freddie laughed. "No, listen. You know how we do about eight things, right? Windows, siding, roofing, patios, stone work, and stuff?"

"Yeah," Troy said in anticipation.

"Well, what we should do is cross-train everybody so eventually everyone can do every service. 'Cause sometimes we have a lot of one thing to do, or a big job of one thing, so I am short on someone who can do it. So let's say we get a big stone work job. What I'll do is put my best stone guy, Felix, on the job, and another guy who doesn't know anything about stone work. Then the green guys can learn from the best. We'll have to throw Felix a couple more bucks, 'cause his helper will be slow at first, but it'll be worth it in the long run. What do you think?" Freddie asked, taking a breath.

"Sweet!" Troy said. "That will solve a problem we have, and we can do more with less guys in the long run."

"Alright, so I'll start doing it right away," Freddie said, again satisfied he was making a difference.

At the next company meeting, after all the excitement from each department's reports, Troy piped up. "Guys, I have a special presentation to make," he said, getting their attention. "I found this, and it meant a lot to me. I hope it does to you, too," he went on, holding a large framed poster in front of him. I'm going to hang it here by the front door, and I want you all to think of it every time you pass through the door."

Then Troy turned it around for all to see. It read:

"A man that works with his hands is a laborer.
A man that works with his hands and his brain is a craftsman.
But a man that works with his hands, his brain
and his heart, is an artist."

– Louis Nizer, Architect.

"Ahhh's" and "Ummm's" came from the team as they finished reading. Troy let them be with it for a long moment. "Ladies and gentlemen, I want to be an artist. How about you?" he asked. Heads nodded. "Freddie, hang this up for me, will you?"

There were a few laughs, and the team broke up until the next week. They all looked forward to the weekly meetings.

"Sandra, can I talk with you in my office?" Troy said.

"Well, this is kind of unusual. What's up?' she asked.

"Sandra, you know I love you. You have been my rock here for 3½ years, and taken care of me," Troy started.

"Uh-oh," she said, sensing something was coming.

"No, no, listen. You have done an excellent job in everything you do. Often I notice things you do that you think I don't notice. And I'm sure there are a million things you do that I don't notice. But I know you are here 100 percent. But lately, you've been working hard, and still, with all the hours you put in, you are struggling to keep up. We're not even at our goal yet," he said.

Sandra listened intently, and a tear came to her eye.

"So I don't want you to take this any way but helpful. It's time to split your job. I want to hire an accountant, and relieve you from those duties. Then you can focus on customer service, setting sales calls, and working with the subs and suppliers as all those jobs grow." He stopped there and watched her for a reaction.

"But I've always done the accounting," she said. Troy was silent. She held back the tears. Then she started to nod. "You're right... okay... it would be better for everyone," she said.

After a few minutes, Troy hugged her and thanked her for being so understanding. He promised that he would never let her down.

Troy continued to listen to audio programs, like the one that he found in his truck one day. He continued to read his blue journal and write more in it. Each day he worked on himself, and positive changes kept happening for him, and at his company.

He hired a CPA, a Certified Public Accountant. Sandra had taught herself accounting, and was pretty good when they were small. But the new accountant was way ahead of Sandra. The new CPA began cost accounting each job to see which jobs they made a lot on, which ones they made a little on, and which they lost money on. They adjusted their pricing and strategies accordingly, to improve.

She also came up with a Key Performance Indicator for each department, and they educated each employee on what they were being measured by. They posted the numbers each week or month as appropriate, and gave bonuses to some employees based on them.

Danny continued to show his commitment, and he learned a lot. Troy promoted him to lead man. Troy was especially proud of Danny, and felt he was lucky to have Danny working for him.

Kara was "promoted," and took on the Human Resources duties as the company grew. Before Troy knew it, the company had 29 employees, plus the subcontractors they worked with.
"Freddie, look at this," Troy said.

Freddie looked at the plans Troy rolled out. "I thought we didn't want to do new construction?"

"Well, this is one exception. I think we're going to build us a new home," Troy told his main man.

"Seriously?" Freddie said.

"I think so. I'm looking at a lot in the new commercial park. I haven't made up my mind yet, so don't say anything to anyone yet, okay?"

It had been half a dozen months or more since Troy had hired Hammy and Helen. "What did we wind up with for sales this month?" Troy asked Hammy. He always loved to ask, because most often it was a higher number than he had ever heard before.

"$321,533.00! The biggest month ever!" Hammy answered. The two men high fived each other awkwardly and laughed.

As Troy left the office that night, he looked around the office, turned the light out and said to himself, "We're on our way."

"Do you realize you've been home by 6 p.m. for dinner for two weeks in a row?" Karissa asked Troy as she passed the vegetables. Troy gave her a satisfying smile.

Chapter 24
Back to the Park

Troy walked out to his truck early in the morning. There was a note on the window:

"Meet me in the park. Same place.
– Cy

P.S. As you know, I take mine black."

Troy was excited to see Cy. He had been wondering when his old friend would come around again. Troy stopped at the coffee shop to get coffee. "I'll take two sandwiches this morning, Chris," Troy called out. "Just in case," he said to himself.

Troy pulled up to the same spot in the park they had met at many months earlier. But he didn't see Cy at the picnic table. He turned to grab the cardboard tray off the front seat, and when he looked up again at the table, Cy was there. "He's quick… and crafty," Troy thought.

"Good morning, Cy," Troy said, as he approached the table.

"Good man," Cy said, as he reached for his coffee.

"I got you a sandwich, too."

"Oh, uh, no thanks. I shouldn't. No telling what would happen," Cy told him.

"Things have been going fantastic!" Troy started.

"You are three quarters of the way to your goal, I hear," Cy said. "I am proud of you, Troy. You've made a lot of progress."

"Well, I have this plan to build a new building for the company," Troy said with excitement. He told Cy all about it, but he knew something was wrong as he did. Cy just didn't get as excited as Troy was. "What's wrong with that idea?" Troy said.

"Maybe nothing," Cy said.

"Or maybe something. I want to know what you think," Troy said.

Cy took another sip of coffee and swallowed patiently. He put his cup down and said, "Okay, look. You just got started. I understand you're excited, but building or moving into a new building costs way more than you think it will. Sure, it'll be fantastic. In fact, I've seen many businesses blossom when they move to new, more suitable, beautiful, functional places. And that may be the case for you. But don't get ahead of yourself."

Troy was disappointed. It's not what he wanted to hear. Cy went on. "Many contractors are rich in July and broke in January, aren't they?" he asked.

"Yeah, I guess," Troy said, still feeling like his balloon was popped.

"A lot of business owners think that just because they are selling $3.5 million worth of services like you, they have tons of money to throw around – so they throw it around. Then they go out of business. Listen, Troy. Handling all that money is a great responsibility. You are the steward of over $300,000 a month now. It is an awesome responsibility that many people are counting on you to get right. Remember what I told you, that a business makes money when it consumes less value than it takes in?"

"Well, you didn't say it that way," Troy said.

"Well, now I am. By spending lots of money on a new building, and all the stuff that goes with it – phone systems, a network for computers, furniture, etc, etc, etc. etc..."

"I get it," Troy said.

"You'll make it harder to make money. In fact, you will find it is incredibly easy to spend your 12 percent, and wind up with nothing."

Troy sat there, quiet.

"You basically made no money for 12 years, right?" Cy asked.

"Right."

"Well, if you make your sales goal, and still make no money, will you be happy?"

Troy paused. "No," he admitted.

"Troy, whether you are busted or making money, you must be wise with your money. You must be cautious, and thrifty. When they start making money, many business owners start thinking differently about expenses. They think they're on a gravy train and can absorb whatever random expense comes along – whether the expense is on purpose or by accident. They can't delay gratification, and they buy this, and buy that. Then they find they look good to all their friends, but they're broke, up to their eyeballs in debt, and unhappy."

"Well, I need more office space," Troy said.

"Fine. There are other ways to accomplish that. You can always build a building later, when you know beyond a shadow of a doubt that you can handle it financially."

"How can I get more office space without moving?" Troy asked.

"You're a smart kid. Figure it out," Cy challenged.

Troy drew a long breath, and let it out. He looked like he had something to ask, but didn't know how. Finally he just let it out. "Cy, when do I get to make some money?"

Cy laughed.

"It's not funny!" Troy said, carefully.

"Remember I told you that you wouldn't make money for a while? Well, this is the while," Cy told him.

"Why? We're selling a lot," Troy protested, knowing he was being a bit childish in a way, but he made some fun out of it.

"Because you are investing in your infrastructure, people, receivables, marketing, and so on. Maybe you need to go back and read your notes, Troy."

Troy suddenly got serious. He didn't want Cy to think he hadn't listened the first time. "I have Cy, and I knew that. It's just that it's frustrating to wait. I mean, we don't have any money left after everyone gets paid and we pay our bills. Some days I wonder if I'm doing it right," Troy said.

"You know what you get when you mix patience and courage?" Cy asked.

"No."

"Persistence. Ninety percent of businesspeople who failed weren't defeated – they simply gave up."

Troy acknowledged Cy with a determined nod.

"Don't give up, Troy. Ever. Even when you do everything right, it takes time. Keep checking your performance numbers for each department, and cost accounting the jobs, and working to make each department as efficient as possible. And I want to give you two more things you should measure." Troy got his blue book out.

Cy went on. "Measure your breakeven. That's how much businesses you have to do just to break even. The formula is: fixed costs divided by gross profit margin. Fixed costs are what you have to pay even if you do no jobs – like marketing, office salaries, *rent, overhead...*" Cy stressed the words, referring to their earlier conversation.

"Gross profit is when you take a typical job and subtract all the direct job costs out, like labor, materials and sales commission — and you get a percentage left. That's gross profit. Figure it out, Troy."

Troy didn't know the answer, but he wrote the formula in his book.

"Then figure it each month to see how your spending decisions make it harder or easier to make money."

Troy sighed. He thought he was over the hump. His business was growing and he was hoping it was that easy.

"It's another paradox, Troy. It's easy, and it's not that easy," Cy said.

"How'd you know what I was thinking?" Troy asked.

"Ahh, I know." Cy shrugged the question off.

"The other thing I want you to measure is your spread," Cy said.

"My what?"

"Your spread. This is the single most important number that I looked at during all my years in business," Cy reflected to his student.

"What is it?"

"It's the number you get when you add cash and receivables, and subtract payables. Measure it every two weeks and compare it to what it was in previous months. When it is going up, you're doing better. When it's going down, you're doing worse than before. I always decided if and how much more — or less — I would take in pay by the way the spread was expanding or contracting. I would always leave a cash cushion in the company. That's called a financial shock absorber. We got to the point where we paid our bills on receipt for many years," Cy reflected proudly.

"Okay, I got it. I'll measure it every two weeks," Troy promised.

"Troy, here's another paradox. The money is the way to tell if you're doing it right, and profit is important. But don't do it for the money."

Troy was listening. Cy continued, "If you build your machine, measure the results, take care of your employees and train them to take care of the customers, the money will come."

"I believe you," Troy said. "I mean, I believe when you say I won't make money for a while," he added, laughing heartily.

Cy laughed too. "See, I told you," Cy said.

The seasons were changing and it wasn't so warm anymore. The park bench felt cold under them. A cool wind stirred, blowing the pages in Troy's journal over.

"There are a few more things you need to know right now, Troy." Cy looked up at the sky. "Let's finish up before it starts raining."

Troy looked up at the sky. It didn't look like rain to him.

"Troy, you need to do more in the way of a structured customer service program," Cy told him.

"But we have the Bobber system and our values. What more do we need?" Troy asked, a little puzzled.

"Those are great steps. The Bobber system is great for production. And the values are great, but they don't tell your people exactly how to behave in situations with your customers. As you get more employees, it becomes even more important. You'll need to be more specific about what great service is. You can't have everyone interpreting it a different way."

Troy wrote notes. "Where am I going to get that? Just make it up?" Troy asked the sage.

"You could. But you don't have to," Cy repeated, again looking up.

"What do you mean, I don't have to?"

"You'll figure it out," Cy said, zipping his jacket up a few more inches.

"Troy, I have a few more things I want you to write down quickly. As you progress, I want you to visit these ideas and think on them. Okay?" Cy instructed, with some urgency.

"Okay," Troy said obediently, as he flipped to a new page in his blue journal.

"You need to guard your company's reputation. It's hard to get a good reputation, and easy to lose it. And what your people do creates the company's reputation. Guard it."

"And that's why you're saying that a customer service program is so important then, right?" Troy asked, still writing.

"Yes," Cy said, seeming in a rush.

"Are you ready to write the next thing?" Cy asked Troy.

"Okay, go ahead."

"Your ability to develop relationships and contacts is vital. And your ability to get along with others, and see things from their point of view, is crucial. And if your people think you're becoming a jerk, they will leave you," Cy rattled.

"They're all related points, right?" Troy asked, still writing.

"Related, but different," Cy said. "Are you ready for the next thing?"

"Well… I…, " Troy said, struggling to keep up.

"Just write for now, you can think later," Cy said in a rush. "Be loyal to the people who helped you and stood by you."

"I know that," Troy said.

"Loyalty takes on new meaning as life happens and there is a test," Cy said, like he knew what he was talking about.

"And lastly, get some new friends."

Troy looked up. "What?"

"Get some new friends," Cy repeated.

"Isn't that disloyal?" Troy said.

"I didn't say anything about ditching your old friends, Troy. I simply mean that you should find people who have qualities you want to have, or who have attained goals like the ones you're trying to achieve. Don't be fake. But if you make friends with other successful people, they can teach you a lot," Cy explained.

Troy struggled with what Cy meant, and looked at him for clarification.

"Am I your friend?" Cy asked, to make his point.

"Yes, and more," Troy said, now understanding what Cy meant.

"Well," Cy paused, "I'm not going to be here forever."

A drop of rain hit the table between them, making a small, dark circle in the dry, wooden top. Then another. Then a larger one hit the page in the open journal. Troy closed it, protecting its contents.

"You should go," Cy said. Troy wondered if this was it. Was this his last encounter with Cy? Before he could think too long on it, the rain drops got larger and faster. Both men stood up, and Troy stepped over the picnic table seat to go for his truck. He took four steps away, and turned to see if Cy was following. Cy wasn't. He stood by the table in the rain.

"Go on," Cy told him over the sound of the rain.

Troy took a few more steps towards his truck, holding the blue book against his chest. Then he stopped and turned around to Cy again.

"Cy!" he called out. "How did you know it was going to rain?"

Cy yelled back. "Experience."

When Troy got to his truck he looked back at the picnic table, but Cy was gone. Panic struck Troy as he realized that he still never said thank you.

Leaning against the trunk of a tall spruce tree, Cy watched Troy's truck pull away and disappear into the hard rain. It was temporary shelter from the rain for now, until the rain dripped through the thick needles above him.

Cy slid his back down the trunk and huddled up. He folded his arms across his knees and put his head down. A memory began to come into view. He was 14 years old. He had a school economics project to work on, explaining how people made a living. He was at the kitchen table telling his parents what he decided his project would be on. His dad had many jobs in his life, never seeming to be able to stay at one place. He drank from time to time, which didn't help.

"I'm going to do my project on something I know really well," the young Cy said around dinner. "I've been very successful with my paper route. I have more money in my pocket than anyone else at school. And I can buy my own stuff. I'm just going to tell everyone how I do it," Cy declared, with some excitement.

His dad looked up, and serious as he could be, he said, "Don't you rub their noses in that. You're not a know-it-all, boy. Don't brag, 'cause nobody cares."

After everyone else had fallen asleep, Troy pulled the blue book out from his bag. He sat on the couch in the quiet living room, with just a soft light from the hall washing in. He opened up his journal to the pages he wrote in that day. The pages were still damp. He read, and thought. A deep sadness washed over him. How could he be so rude? Cy had come into his life, and changed it forever. How could he ever say thank you now? How could he ever repay him?

He sat there in the stillness for over an hour. He resolved that the only way to repay Cy now, was to not let him down.

Chapter 25

Milestones

Troy worked on his business as time passed. He monitored his 'spread,' as Cy had instructed him to, and soon came to see the value in doing so. After several months, he went to his new accountant.

"We have a new paycheck to make each week," he said.

"Who is the new employee?" she asked.

"Me. Please put me on the payroll for $100,000 a year." Troy went back to his office, and thought about the milestone he had just hit.

He solved his company's space problem. He expanded the offices into the shop space in the back, and rented the building next door for additional shop, yard and parking space. He paid attention to the aesthetics of the new facility when fitting it up, and it came out looking clean and classy.

Troy fumbled with a customer service program for a while, until he found a program he could just use as is, called "Wow Service." It was perfect.

The leads rolled in, and Hammy built an effective sales force ever bigger, including two female salespeople, which was unusual in their business. Mr. Singer kept a crew busy at the university almost constantly. Sales grew to $397,000 a month.

"Almost there," Troy said to the team at a weekly meeting.

"Here we go!" Troy said to his three children across the row of seats, as the front of the plane lifted off the runway. He held Karissa's hand as the ground fell away. "Our first real vacation," he whispered, as he kissed her cheek.

Troy told Sandra to call him on vacation if they needed him. Nobody called.

"Welcome back!" Sandra said. As Troy walked in, Hammy, Kara and Sandra stood up, as if they were waiting for him to arrive. They were all beaming. Kara took Troy's hand and led him over to the sales board. The month had just ended. Sandra pointed to the total, which was circled three times in blue. It read: $423,000.

"Can you believe it?" Sandra asked. Troy stared at the number for a long moment, thinking of Cy.

Hammy interrupted Troy's thoughts. "What do you think?" he said.

Troy cracked a wide smile. "I want to thank you all. You guys are the best team in the business," he said gratefully. "This week, we celebrate!" And celebrate they did, including all the employees.

Troy kept an eye on his spread. It was expanding. That week he took his first ever distribution check. As he drove home, he felt freer than he ever had in his life.

Chapter 26

The Last Lesson

Troy hurried out of his truck and ran up to the glass door, just as Chris was locking it.

Chris greeted his friend. "Hey buddy! How you doin'? I shut the grill down. What do you need?" Chris asked Troy, as he let him in.

"I knew you were closing, but I thought I'd steal a cup of joe, last minute, if I could," Troy said.

"I got you covered my friend," Chris said, as he turned his back to get the last coffee of the day. "So how you been doin'?"

"Man, I gotta tell you," Troy said, slow and sincerely to his friend. "God bless America. If you work hard and smart, and help other people, dreams come true."

Chris turned around with his coffee. The shop was quiet, except for the sound of someone clanking pots and cleaning up in the back. The two men spoke plainly to each other.

"I know," Chris said. "That's why I came here from Romania. God bless America, brother."

Troy put two bucks down on the counter.

Chris waved it off. "It's on me," he said.

"Thanks, man," Troy said, as he lifted the paper cup to toast Chris. "Hey, you don't mind if I sit and make a couple phone calls, do you?"

"Not at all. I gotta go close the kitchen. I locked the door, so just let yourself out when you want," Chris said.

Troy walked over to sit in a booth with his cell phone in his hand. There was Cy. Troy was surprised, and suddenly his heart sped up. He thought he'd never see Cy again. But this time, he wasn't going to let this opportunity go by. He approached the booth and sat down. "Cy, I am so happy to see you."

"It's great to see you, Troy," Cy said, his two hands wrapped around a coffee cup. Troy noticed that Cy looked different. He wasn't sure what it was.

"Cy, I don't really know how to say this. But I will be forever grateful for your help."

Cy smiled at him. "I know."

"No, you don't. I mean, you… well, you saved my life," Troy said, looking right at Cy with respect and gratitude. "And you made a difference for so many people. I can't thank you enough."

"I want to thank *you*, Troy. You made a difference for me. One you may never understand," Cy told him.

"What did I do for you?" Troy asked.

"You made me complete," Cy said. Cy was right. Troy didn't understand, and he sat there wondering what Cy meant.

"You made your goal?" Cy asked.

"Well, we made a month, and we're right on track for $5 million," Troy said proudly, wondering if that was what made Cy 'complete.' "I can see that we can do more, Cy. I… I really think that we can do $10 million," he said thoughtfully. Cy smiled broadly.

Troy knew that if he had questions, he had to ask them now. "How do I get there?" Troy asked.

"The same way you got to $5 million," Cy said.

Troy noticed that Cy had the same enthusiasm and meaning in his voice, but less urgency and energy. "It's not that complicated, Troy. Once you know how to do it, and you obviously do, then you can bend the future to any vision you set with the same process," Cy said, sitting back comfortably. Troy listened.

"That's it? Aren't there new rules or something?" Troy asked.

"Nope." Cy sipped his coffee. "You set a new goal and challenge it – make sure it is realistic. Envision how your organization will look, write it down, and use the same processes to call the future into being as you did the first time. Same thing, just a different scale."

Troy felt like he should be writing, but his journal was in the truck.

"Oh, I have something for you," Troy said excitedly. He stood up. "I have to go get it. I'll be right back." Troy took a few steps and then turned back to Cy. "Wait, you aren't going anywhere. I mean, you're gonna' be here when I get back in 30 seconds, right?"

"I think so," Cy assured him. Satisfied, Troy unlocked the coffee shop door and ran out to his truck. He came back in 30 seconds, as he said he would, and put the blue journal down on the table.

"This is for you," Troy said. "I've been carrying it around for weeks."

Cy looked down at a very small box wrapped in shiny blue gift wrap with gold lines on it. The corners were worn from being in Troy's bag for a long time. Cy unwrapped it slowly and carefully. It was a felt box, like a ring box. Cy slowly opened it. Inside was a gold coin. Cy lifted it out. One side depicted a classic image — a beautiful angel, with wings and a halo. Cy flipped it over, and the other side read: "You made a difference."

Cy sat, staring at the coin, flipping it over front to back, again and again. A tear filled Cy's eye. They sat for a long time.

"Thank you," Cy finally whispered. "You saved my life."

Diffusing the emotion of the moment, Cy perked up. "Hey, you have your book there," he said, motioning to the journal on the table. "Open it up. I have a few more things for you to write down," he said.

"You have more?" Troy asked, flipping to a new page towards the back of the book, and getting ready to write what he considered to be a bonus.

"Well, I just want to make sure you keep it together," Cy said.

"Okay, I'm ready," Troy said, pen to paper.

"A few things will happen over time, Troy. You have to watch out for them, and make sure they aren't the end of your business," Cy cautioned.

"Like what?"

"Well, first, when some businesspeople become successful, they go into the marketplace being defensive, trying to protect what they have, instead of staying on the offense to build their team and services better all the time. When it comes to innovation, positioning your company in the marketplace, and embracing change, you have to stay on the offense. Do you understand?"

"I understand," Troy said, looking up from his writing.

"And you have to stay flexible," Cy continued. "Don't get locked into 'how' you do things, or where or when. There are lots of ways to accomplish your goals. And things change. You may have a good way of doing it now, but strengths have a way of becoming weaknesses over time. Stay flexible," Cy said.

"And don't overdiversify. Business people have a tendency to think that because they're good at one business, they'd be good at any business. Then they start second and third businesses that fail, because they don't put the same effort and time into them as they did in the one they originally succeeded with. Smart diversification is when the second business shares the same knowledge, talent, skills, or customers as the first."

Troy noticed how Cy was speaking. He seemed to be using all of his energy to get his message out, yet he was comfortable at the same time. Cy looked like a man who was overtired, but loved what he was doing.

"You ready?" Cy said.

"Huh? Oh yeah," Troy said, looking back down at his journal and finishing the sentence he was writing. "Go ahead."

"As time goes by, you and your staff will have a tendency to make things more complicated than they have to be. You must resist this. You must create a culture of simplicity. And still, every once in a while, you'll have to overhaul how things are done to get the clutter out, and make your system's clean and elegant again."

Troy looked up.

"Just write. You'll see what I mean later," Cy told him, letting out a weak laugh. Troy finished writing the idea and looked up. Cy looked tired.

Troy asked, "What was the name of your remodeling company?"

"My remodeling company?" Cy asked.

"Yeah. When you were in business," Troy said.

"What makes you think I was in the remodeling business?" Cy asked the young man.

"You weren't?"

"Not even close."

Troy looked at him for a long moment. "Huh."

"Over time, Troy, things are going to happen. All kinds of things. That's a given. How you respond is what's important. Don't procrastinate facing problems. Solve them in your head first, because often that's where the problems really are. Then ask for help from the people you trust. Remember, you aren't alone, even though you're the leader."

Troy soaked up Cy's words.

"And don't compromise your values."

"I know that," Troy said.

"I know you know it. But for many, the difference is how you behave when the tests come. And they will come."

Cy took a long pause. Troy caught up writing his notes, and looked up. Still, Cy didn't speak. He flipped the gold coin over in his hand, studying it. "This is not a dress rehearsal, Troy."
"What do you mean?"

Cy flipped the coin again. "Listen to me. Your business should support your life, not *be* your life," he said. Troy sat, feeling he was in for a final lesson.

Cy spoke slowly. "You have to live while you are still alive. Success is not something you get one day; it's something you become now. You must learn to be happy now. Don't wait."

Cy sat peacefully, slowly turning the coin in his hand. "Life is short, young man. You must live it on purpose, not by chance," the old man said, slowly and deliberately.

"You are on your way to the future, and there are things you don't need to bring with you… like hate, fear, jealousy, and regret."

Troy swallowed hard. Cy spoke ever slower. "Take care of the ones you love. Be a good friend. Help others."

The two men sat in the words for a long while.

Troy knew his time with Cy was over. "Who sent you here to help me?" he asked softly.

Cy looked up at him with kind eyes. "You did."

Cy turned the coin in his hand for the last time. "I can't take this with me where I am going. I want you to keep it," Cy said, handing the coin to Troy.

Troy held his hand out, trembling. Cy pressed it in his palm.

"Where are you going?" Troy asked.

"Home."

Chapter 27

Going Home

A white mist enveloped him. A figure began to appear, approaching him. As it got closer, he could make out a man. It was his father. He came to him, and stood close.

"Dad. I just wanted you to be proud of me," he said.

"I was proud of you, son, beyond measure. I told everyone I met about you."

"Why didn't you ever tell me?" he asked.

"Because I wanted you to be proud of me."

"I was proud of you, Dad. I was proud of you for being my Dad." The father hugged his son tight.

As the beautiful angel came into view, she smiled, and her soft wing brushed him in.

Chapter 28

Legacy

An old man sat on the dock at the lake in the sun. The wooden boards clucked with the footsteps of the approaching younger man.

"How are you doing today?"

"My left hip has been bothering me, but I'm fine. Did you bring your book?"

The young man produced a blue journal. He opened the front cover, where he had written his name. "Doug Morey."

The old man turned a coin in his hand as he spoke. "When you create a successful business, you are improving the lives of hundreds, thousands, or even millions of people. There is no higher calling."

About the Author

Larry Janesky is an authority on creating and building businesses for the benefit of business owners, employees and customers. Larry is a highly successful author of five books, acclaimed speaker, inventor with 24 patents, and business leader with 27 years of real world accountability and success.

He began his business adventure as a self-employed carpenter at age 17, and built his first house at 18. In the 27 years since then, he has discovered what he teaches today – that in order for business owners to grow their businesses, they must grow personally.

He has the wisdom that can only come from someone who has struggled, failed, become a 'learning machine', and persisted for 27 years. The results show the power of what Larry knows about business, and wants to share with you.

Today, Larry owns the industry-leading Basement Systems Inc. and its six sister businesses; an award-winning, successful-in-every-way 60 million dollar enterprise based in Seymour Connecticut, with 345 dealers in 6 countries – and Larry has *big* plans for the future!

Larry lives in suburban Connecticut with Wendy, his lovely wife of 18 years, and their three children – Tanner, Chloe and Autumn.

Larry's goal is to improve the lives of millions of business owners, their employees, their customers, and humanity in general, through business education, development and excellence.

To find out more about Larry's award winning businesses, go to –

Basement Systems®, Inc.
Basement waterproofing
basementsystems.com

CleanSpace®
Dirt crawl space repair
dirtcrawlspace.com

Total Basement Finishing™
Basement finishing
totalbasementfinishing.com

Foundation Supportworks™
Foundation structural repair
foundationsupportworks.com

Dr. Energy Saver™
Home energy contracting
drenergysaver.com

Relia-Serve™ Corporation
Business coaching
relia-serve.com

Thank you for experiencing ***The Highest Calling****!*

At *TheHighestCallingBook.com* you can:

- Post your comments on the book.
- Recommend the book to your friends and schools with a book summary.
- Get 'The Highest Calling' audiobook recorded by the author.
- Get Larry's 'Wow! Service' program.
- Get unique and powerful Business Building Exercises written by Larry.
- Sign up for updates on future work by Larry.
- Send Larry a message.
- Sign up for Larry's popular 'Think Daily' & 'Think Daily for Businesspeople' messages – *free!*

Please visit!